The HAPPY WARRIOR

The life story of
Sir Winston Churchill

The HAPPY WARRIOR

The life story of
Sir Winston Churchill

as told through Great Britain's *EAGLE* comic of the 1950s

Commentary by Richard M. Langworth CBE

LEVENGER
PRESS

With grateful acknowledgment to

Winston S. Churchill

for sharing this life story
of his grandfather
with new generations

This facsimile edition published by Levenger Press
420 South Congress Avenue
Delray Beach, Florida 33445 USA
www.Levengerpress.com

First Edition 2008

ISBN 978-1-929154-34-0

Cover and book design by Danielle Furci
Mim Harrison, Editor

Printed in the USA

Contents

The Eagle That Dared

C olin Frewin remembers vividly what Fridays meant as a young lad growing up in postwar Britain.

"Every Friday was a big Friday," Frewin recalls. "It's when we learned of the next episode of Dan Dare's adventures. What would he do next?"

Throughout Britain, from 1950 to 1969, thousands of youngsters like Frewin would race to their local newsagents every Friday, pence in hand and sometimes parents in tow, to buy their latest issue of the *Eagle* comic, featuring the adventures of Dan Dare, Pilot of the Future.

But this was no ordinary comic strip. This was something the likes of which the country— in fact, the world—had never seen.

Adventures on every page

Each issue of the *Eagle* was chockablock with adventures for boys. There was news on the Eagle Club that all readers were invited to join (60,000 of them did by the second issue).

If you had done a kind or heroic deed, your teacher or family might suggest you for the Mug of the Month distinction.

Plus the latest adventures of Extra Special Agent Harris Tweed, and of Terry Walls and other characters as well as Dan Dare. Tips from the pros on boxing and jiu-jitsu, and instructions on how to keep a goldfish. A hobbies corner ("collecting cheese labels" was one). And frequently, a photo competition or word game.

You could order a complete mint set of British Colonial stamps ("please tell your parents you are ordering"). Or send in the box tops from the Sugar Puffs cereal to get the miniature plastic cowboy and Indian FREE!

If you were very good, and had done a kind or heroic deed, your teacher or family might suggest you for the Mug of the Month distinction, which earned you a write-up with your photo.

Then in the center were those amazing cutaway diagrams of trains and planes and aircraft carriers that were as detailed as an engineer's. And even the back cover, something there—another adventure! This time of real action heroes, Montgomery or Nelson or Churchill. All those pages—16, at least! All that fantastic color!

Best of all, all theirs.

The *Eagle* belonged not to their parents or their teachers (though both, for reasons we shall discover, heartily approved of it), but to *them*—to Frewin and his mates and thousands of English boys like them. Even the editor's note inside was addressed to them.

And so for this new generation of Britons, Fridays spilled over into Saturdays and then Sundays, clusters of boys gathered together to share in the adventures of an exciting new age.

All of which owed its start to a parish priest in England's northwest county of Lancashire.

'A new Elizabethan Age'

Reverend Marcus Morris, the vicar of St. James's Church in the seacoast town of Southport, saw a need, and then an opportunity, for comics with a conscience. He believed that the youth of 1950s Britain needed a publication that inculcated standards and morals as it entertained with action and adventure.

The *Eagle* was not hatched overnight. Its genesis followed a twisting, sometimes torturous path. It eventually took the Oxford-educated vicar to London and, after a suitable number of rejections, to Hulton Press on Fleet Street.

> The Eagle presaged Britain's technological dexterity in the realms of aviation, defense, and architecture.

What made the *Eagle* soar above other comic strips of the time was its quality—the paper, the printing, the color, the writing and, most especially, the art. Frank Hampson was the co-founder of the comic and the head artist of Dan Dare and other *Eagle* action heroes. His first studio was a converted bakery in Southport. In a 1974 interview (Hampson died in 1985), he said of Dan Dare: "I wanted to give [young people] something that made the future more hopeful." He also had a hunch that space travel would launch in the not-too-distant future.

"They were so different from the comics we had been used to," says Paul Courtenay, a retired officer of the British Army who remembers "avidly" reading the weekly adventures as a teenager. "The others were all rubbish. The *Eagle* was a breath of fresh air." And it signaled a headwind of a larger magnitude.

"It was a new Elizabethan age in Britain," explains Frewin, who today is the Chief Executive of the Dan Dare Corporation and the owner of the *Eagle* comic. "We had come out of the war and had a new young queen and new horizons to explore."

The *Eagle* was itself a feat of derring-do. It captured, celebrated, and at times uncannily presaged Britain's technological dexterity in the realms of aviation, defense, and architecture. The trains, boats, planes, and buildings that appeared as the center cutaways of each issue were more than fanciful designs. They were based on actual models that Hampson and his team had created. They were also extraordinarily well detailed. In fact, the cutaway of a nuclear submarine revealed its inner workings so splendidly that the Admiralty demanded to know the source of such precision.

As Frewin says, "It was based on existing reports of the submarine, plus a little imagination and guesswork as to how things would work."

Wordsworth meets Dan Dare

What the creators of the *Eagle* probably could not have imagined was just how well their idea would work.

Whatever else happened in the world on 14 April 1950, there was this: the first issue of the *Eagle* hit the newsagents in England and sold 900,000 copies. The Pilot of the Future had rocketed to fame.

Readers were encouraged to clip the reminder that was printed, coupon-fashion, on the editor's page and to take it to their newsagents, asking them to order the *Eagle* for them every week. Eventually the *Eagle* would produce offspring—first *Girl*, then *Robin* and *Swift*—so that girls and younger siblings could have their own publications as well.

> "The Greatest EAGLE News Yet!" was the advance notice that "The Happy Warrior" received.

The *Eagle* maintained its high-flying trajectory, selling three-quarters of a million copies on average each week. Dan Dare would soon even have his own radio show, broadcast on Radio Luxembourg.

Even the Pilot of the Future could not know about a twenty-first-century phenomenon called social networking, but that's exactly what the *Eagle* created. In its own, pre-Internet way, it formed a virtual forum for young boys. Plus it had the blessings of Mum and Dad and the headmaster.

When, for instance, readers asked where the title "The Happy Warrior" came from for the Churchill series, Reverend Morris told his young readers that it was from a poem by Wordsworth. He encouraged them to have their teachers help them find it. "It is well worth reading," he advised.

"It was a thrill," says Frewin, summing up that Friday frisson of *Eagle* excitement. "Youngsters were as dazzled as their parents. My father would read the issues after I did."

Frewin's father had been a pilot in the Royal Air Force during World War II. When Winston Churchill died in 1965, he took his son to the funeral. "We queued for eight hours to go past the coffin," Frewin says. He was only four when the *Eagle* debuted "The Happy Warrior," the weekly back-cover chronicle of Churchill's life that ran from 4 October 1957 to 6 September 1958. Those covers are reproduced in this work in their entirety, exactly as they appeared in the original editions, just the way Frewin first read them at the age of eight. (His father had kept all the back issues of *Eagle*, a custom that fathers and sons all over England happily hewed to.)

"The Greatest EAGLE News Yet!" was the advance notice that "The Happy Warrior" received, because Churchill was, proclaimed the *Eagle*, "the most famous man in the world." Readers were again advised to alert their local newsagents, as without a reserved copy, they may be out of luck. The estimable Frank Bellamy drew the series, which debuted in Volume 8, Number 40.

"On the one cover was this fictitious hero, Dan Dare. On the other was this real hero, Winston Churchill," says Frewin. It seems a fitting pairing.

Frewin describes Dan Dare as "a superhero with old-fashioned values." He was a twentieth-century vision of the future, with morals firmly rooted in the century past— rather like the real hero named Churchill.

A manifesto for all ages

Although the original *Eagle* ceased publication in 1969, its legacy lives on in unexpected places. Some of the young lads studying those cutaways became England's new crop of architects and engineers. In their work can be seen the stamp of an *Eagle*. In the *Eagle*, in turn, can be seen a precursor of today's graphic novel.

Perhaps its greatest legacy resides in the minds and hearts of those thousands of youngsters who pored over its pages, and in the contributions to country and community they went on to make.

In the very first issue of *Eagle*, on the editor's page, Marcus Morris issued his Eagle Club "manifesto." Members of the club would…

> **a)** Enjoy life and help others to enjoy life. They will not enjoy themselves at the expense of others.
>
> **b)** Make the best of themselves. They will develop themselves in body, mind and spirit. They will tackle things for themselves and not wait for others to do things for them.
>
> **c)** Work with others for the good of all around them.
>
> **d)** Always lend a hand to those in need of help. They will not shirk difficult or dangerous jobs.

It would be nice to think that such adventures will go on forever—that, like the last panel of so many pages of the *Eagle*, it is a story to be continued.

*The cover of the issue of 4 October 1957, featuring
the first installment of "The Happy Warrior"*

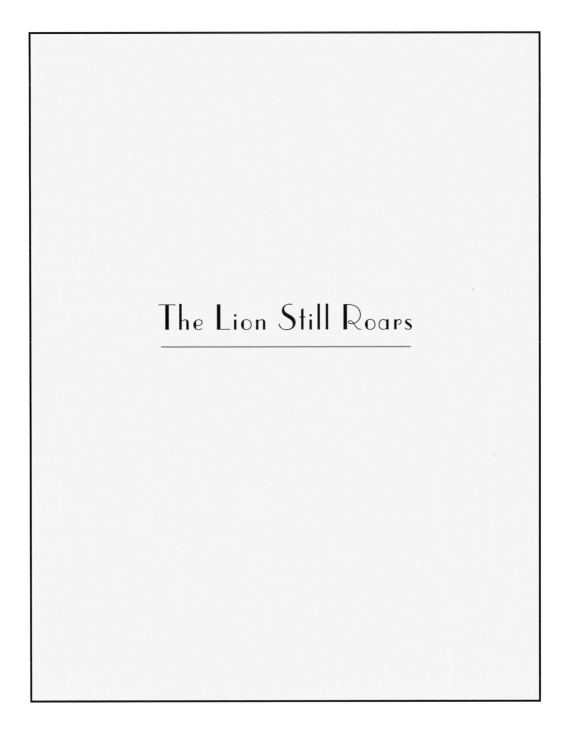

The Lion Still Roars

W hat may strike a seasoned Churchill reader about "The Happy Warrior" is how unlikely it would be for such a comic to appear today, however factual the story it tells.

We live in an iconoclastic age. Values, traditions, and legacies once held sacred are questioned, plumbed, and deconstructed by self-appointed analysts and would-be philosophers. It's unlikely that today anyone would publish a comic commemorating, in purely hagiographic terms, any real-life leader, even Winston Churchill.

William Manchester called the habit of viewing past times through a modern prism "generational chauvinism": the gratuitous assumption that only today's generation is capable of understanding and eradicating "the mess of centuries." Those were in fact the words Clement Attlee, Britain's postwar prime minister, used in 1951 to describe the task before his government. Churchill, then Leader of the Opposition, objected:

> *The mess of centuries—that is all we were. The remark is instructive because it reveals with painful clarity [Attlee's] point of view and sense of proportion. Nothing happened that was any good until they came into office. We may leave out the great struggles and achievements of the past—Magna Carta, the Bill of Rights, Parliamentary institutions, Constitutional Monarchy, the building of our Empire—all these were part of the mess of centuries....But at last a giant and a Titan appeared to clear up the mess of centuries. Alas, he cries, he has had only six years to do it in.[1]*

As Churchill's experience demonstrates, people were decrying the "struggles and achievements of the past" long before today; but the mutterings have grown to a cacophony, amplified by a 24/7 news media and that digital Hyde Park Corner, the World Wide Web.

"The Happy Warrior," first published fifty years ago, had no truck with any of this. Nor was it surprising.

In the 1950s, World War II was as recent as the presidential election of Bill Clinton is today. Nobody had yet published a seriously critical work on the wartime prime minister who had led a Britain alone against Hitler's Third Reich. Even though the effort rendered Britain bankrupt, and postwar governments did little to revive it, Churchill was still a hero to most citizens, every young person, and, of course, the publishers of the *Eagle*.

Valid criticism is part of the historical process, and the advent of questioning works, which began with Field Marshal Alanbrooke's diaries in 1959, was perfectly understandable. Churchill lived a long life and made many mistakes. His successes outweighed his failures, but as a noted scholar of his domestic politics says, "To me it only serves to diminish Churchill to regard him as super-human."[2]

But in 1958, basking in retirement, having just published at age 84 the fourth and final volume of his magisterial *History of the English-Speaking Peoples,* Churchill *seemed* super-human. It's astonishing that he has managed to scale the intervening half century with his reputation still intact, after so many complaints, some of them deserved.

The only hints of criticism in "The Happy Warrior" are the suggestion that Winston traded his English for another boy's Latin at school (4 Oct.) and that it was foolhardy—which it probably was—to defend Crete in World War II (9 May). The shoals on which Churchill briefly went aground—the gold standard and General Strike in the 1920s, die-hard opposition to the India Bill and Gandhi in the early 1930s, over-zealous support of Edward VIII in the 1936 abdication crisis—are all untouched by this account. Of course, it is a war story, not a biography, so successes like settling the Middle East in 1921 or helping write the Irish Treaty in 1922 are similarly omitted.

But even militarily, "The Happy Warrior" is almost universally positive. Churchill is not tagged with the failed Dardanelles expedition, nor any of his lesser controversies in World War I.[3] Unremarked in World War II are his underestimation of German tank tactics (resulting in the fall of France—not that this was his fault) and his confidence in Stalin at Teheran and Yalta (resulting in the Cold War). The fall of Singapore and loss of two capital ships (the battleship HMS *Prince of Wales* and the battlecruiser HMS *Renown*) to Japanese aircraft are mentioned, but without blaming Churchill (23 May).

The comic strip does convey Churchill's surprise at the speed of France's collapse in 1940 and the fall of Tobruk in 1942. Author Clifford Makins missed a wonderful line about Tobruk, when Churchill learned of its loss on a visit to Washington: "I am the most miserable Englishman in America since Burgoyne"—the British general defeated at Saratoga during the American Revolution.[4] Another famous loss line came in 1945, when his wife said the lost election was a blessing in disguise (23 Aug.): "At the moment," Churchill replied, "it appears quite effectively disguised."[5]

'...talks through his nose and cannot pronounce the letter "S" properly'

The comic strip is remarkably accurate on Winston's youth, given what was known at the time—mostly his own writings. In the 1950s, the vast trove of the Churchill Archives at Cambridge was not yet organized, and would not begin to be deeply plumbed by the faithful biographer, Martin Gilbert, for nearly a decade after "The Happy Warrior" was published. There was no evidence, for example, that Churchill's Harrow Latin was much better than he claimed; the Latin paper containing only his name and an ink blot (4 Oct.)

has never surfaced in school archives. Nevertheless, "The Happy Warrior" goes a good way to emphasize the now-certain fact that Winston at school was much better than he himself claimed in his famous autobiography.[6]

His years as a dashing young officer eager to see action are also well covered, even if artist Frank Bellamy gives him a build resembling that of Chuck Norris. Young Churchill was more accurately described by the "dead or alive" Wanted Poster a Boer official drafted in 1899: "Englishman, 25 years old, about 5 ft. 8 in. tall, indifferent build, walks with a forward stoop, pale appearance, red-brownish hair, small and hardly noticeable moustache, talks through his nose and cannot pronounce the letter 'S' properly."[7]

His early battles in Queen Victoria's "little wars" are forthrightly described. Fifty years later, one regrets that space precluded some of Churchill's characteristically magnanimous tributes to the fallen foe at Omdurman: "...as brave men as ever walked the earth. The conviction was borne in on me that their claim beyond the grave in respect of a valiant death was not less good than that which any of our countrymen could make."[8]

The Anglo-Boer War of 1899-1902 and his sensational escape from Boer captivity are well and clearly treated. There was no room for amplifications, which would blunt the charges that fly around about his racism, which was no more than the gratuitous attitude of his generation. In fact, Churchill had remarkably enlightened ideas for a Victorian, typified by his comments following an argument with a racist guard at the Boer prison over black South Africans: "What is the true and original root of Dutch aversion to British rule?...It is the abiding fear and hatred of the movement that seeks to place the native on a level with the white man....The dominant race is to be deprived of their superiority; nor is a tigress robbed of her cubs more furious than is the Boer at this prospect."[9]

The comic skips quickly over Churchill's radical decade when, as a rising young Conservative-turned-Liberal, he took office following the great Liberal landslide of 1906 and fought with Lloyd George for social reform and the welfare state; and when he married Clementine Hozier, the greatest and most beneficent influence over him for the rest of his life (31 Jan.).

Then, suddenly, the Guns of August fire.

The World War I treatment is uncritical but good, and Bellamy's faces are remarkably lifelike. We meet Prime Minister H. H. Asquith, whose lack of decisive leadership doomed the Dardanelles campaign, and eventually his premiership. And Lord Kitchener (31 Jan.), who promises "an assault on Gallipoli by the Army," but in fact failed promptly to send ground troops. And Admiral "Jacky" Fisher, at first more enthusiastic than Churchill about the Dardanelles, but who then changed his mind and resigned, taking Churchill with him in the Cabinet crisis that followed.

"The Happy Warrior" has no room to explain the personal impact of Churchill's resignation, which Clementine vividly recalled: "When he left the Admiralty he thought he was finished. I thought he would never get over the Dardanelles. I thought he would die of grief."[10]

A comic strip has to concentrate on essentials and cannot always be 100 percent faithful to the actual words spoken. When Churchill resigned from the government and went to fight in Flanders, Asquith never said to him, "What a waste! You're throwing your career away!" (14 Feb.) Personally, Asquith was glad to see him go. The comic is accurate on Churchill's close call in the field, leaving his headquarters moments before it was shattered by German shells (21 Feb.), but inaccurate in suggesting that his Army colleagues told him to return to

Parliament. (He really needed no urging.) But for a man in his forties to go off to fight in that desperate war was a revealing testimony to his courage, and here the comic has him exactly right.

'...the stairway which leads to a dark gulf...'

The period between the two world wars is covered in a page, and Adolf Hitler makes his baleful appearance in the run-up to World War II (7 Mar.). The 1930s, when Churchill's lone voice signaled the terror to come, is the period for which he is most revered by many who study him. Unfortunately he plays this role in only one pane, and the quotation is necessarily truncated. Readers may wish to contemplate the full passage, delivered in 1932, seventy days before Hitler took power:

> *Now the demand is that Germany should be allowed to rearm. Do not delude yourselves. Do not let His Majesty's Government believe—I am sure they do not believe—that all that Germany is asking for is equal status....That is not what Germany is seeking. All these bands of sturdy Teutonic youths, marching through the streets and roads of Germany, with the light of desire in their eyes to suffer for their Fatherland, are not looking for status. They are looking for weapons, and, when they have the weapons, believe me they will then ask for the return of lost territories and lost colonies, and when that demand is made it cannot fail to shake and possibly shatter to their foundations every one of the countries I have mentioned, and some other countries I have not mentioned.*[11]

Churchill's urgent warnings during the 1930s encompass some of the finest passages in the English language. The greatest of them all came six months before Munich:

> *I have watched this famous island descending incontinently, fecklessly, the stairway which leads to a dark gulf. It is a fine broad stairway at the beginning, but after a bit the carpet ends. A little farther on there are only flagstones, and a little farther on still these break beneath your feet....if mortal catastrophe should overtake the British Nation and the British Empire, historians a thousand years hence will still be baffled by the mystery of our affairs. They will never understand how it was that a victorious nation, with everything in hand, suffered themselves to be brought low, and to cast away all that they had gained by measureless sacrifice and absolute victory—gone with the wind!*[12]

It is no wonder that Bellamy drew Hitler as a crazed monster. But Hitler was a perceptive fanatic, who judged his opponents shrewdly, and half his military decisions were correct. Fortunately, there was the other half. Contrary to the comic strip, for example, Hitler did not expect the D-Day invasion at Normandy (12 July); he expected it at Calais, and disposed his troops accordingly.

Nor did Hitler say, "We will conquer Europe, Asia, the world...now for Poland, France and England!" (7 Mar.) The reader should be aware that Hitler's aspirations were not global, not at least in 1940. Yet he had made it plain what he *did* want, and that was frightening enough.

What Churchill knew, and his detractors didn't, was that a Britain coexistent with a Nazi continent was unacceptable, for national if not for moral reasons:

You must have diplomatic and correct relations, but there can never be friendship between the British democracy and the Nazi power, that power which spurns Christian ethics, which cheers its onward course by a barbarous paganism, which vaunts the spirit of aggression and conquest, which derives strength and perverted pleasure from persecution, and uses, as we have seen, with pitiless brutality the threat of murderous force. That power cannot ever be the trusted friend of the British democracy. What I find unendurable is the sense of our country falling into the power, into the orbit and influence of Nazi Germany.... I foresee and foretell that the policy of submission will carry with it restrictions upon the freedom of speech and debate in Parliament, on public platforms, and discussions in the Press, for it will be said—indeed, I hear it said sometimes now—that we cannot allow the Nazi system of dictatorship to be criticised by ordinary, common English politicians. Then, with a Press under control, in part direct but more potently indirect, with every organ of public opinion doped and chloroformed into acquiescence, we shall be conducted along further stages of our journey.[13]

Some scholars argue that had he died in 1939, Churchill would be regarded as a minor, brilliant failure. Really? Wouldn't his reputation have depended on how World War II had turned out? Besides, that doesn't take into account his massive historical and biographical writings, his role in World War I, and his reforms as a fighting Liberal.

Few ever argued that there was anyone else to lead the country in May 1940. Absent Churchill, who? This comic was produced, of course, in glorious hindsight, but the reader should consider what Churchill's daughter Mary often says: "Remember—nobody knew in those days whether we were going to win."

'God bless you all'

Win they did, and as befits a tribute to national greatness, "The Happy Warrior" is replete with characters famous in those days, loved and unloved. There is Captain Bernard Warburton-Lee of HMS *Hardy*, who led the attack on Narvik, Norway, and who, mortally wounded, gave the signal: "Continue to engage the enemy." (14 Mar.) There is French General Maxime Weygand (Bellamy makes him unmistakable even from the rear). When Churchill asks, "*Où est la masse de manoeuvre?*," Weygand replies fatefully: "*Aucune.* There is none." (28 Mar.) We see Max Beaverbrook, who truly did "work miracles with the aircraft industry." (18 Apr.) "Some people take drugs," Churchill once said, "I take Max."[14] There are admirals and generals, the capable and the incompetent, all faithfully brought back to life by Makins and Bellamy.

Field Marshal Alanbrooke, Chief of the Imperial General Staff, whose 1959 diaries were the first serious criticism of Churchill's leadership, is cast almost as if Makins read his book in advance. "Brookie" seems always to pose statements that Churchill rebuffs, although in fact Churchill never countermanded his Chiefs of Staff, and Alanbrooke did not say they could not conquer Italy before invading France (12 July). Field Marshal Bernard Montgomery, who brings victory in North Africa, gets his just due (13 June). It is nowhere recorded that Churchill remarked about Montgomery, "In defeat, indomitable; in victory, insufferable"—though it's possible the thought crossed his mind. General Sir Harold Alexander, that quiet giant, is frequently pictured. His telegram, after completing his mission in early 1943, was memorable…

> *Sir: The Orders you gave me on August 15, 1942, have been fulfilled. His Majesty's enemies, together with their impedimenta, have been completely eliminated from Egypt, Cyrenaica, Libya, and Tripolitania. I now await your further instructions.*[15]

…as was Churchill's equally famous reply: "Well, obviously, we shall have to think of something else…"

Churchillian readers will love the way Clifford Makins captures Churchill's best ripostes. When Weygand asks what he will do when the Germans "swarm across the Channel," Churchill replies (as indeed witnesses heard him say): "Drown as many as possible [of them on the way over]—and as for the others, when they crawl ashore we will *frapper sur la tête!*" (4 Apr.) In an age when many British schoolchildren knew some French, Makins saw no need to translate "knock them on the head."

President Roosevelt, who appears at the Atlantic Charter meeting in August 1940 and is engulfed by Pearl Harbor on the same page (23 May), is handled diplomatically. It would have been impolitic, two years after the United States had resisted and ultimately scuttled the Franco-British-Israeli Suez campaign, to fling epithets toward dead American presidents. And after all, America and Russia had won the war that Britain in her most sublime hour didn't lose. So nothing is said of Roosevelt's uneven handling of Churchill, enthusiastically co-signing the Atlantic Charter while resisting any drift toward war, until Pearl Harbor finally forced the issue.

This was a good editorial decision: Roosevelt was as widely admired as Churchill in Britain, maybe more so, and his contributions to the war effort had been prodigious. Hence Churchill's tribute herein, which is a little garbled (16 Aug.). His actual words were: "For us, it remains only to say that in Franklin Roosevelt there died the greatest American friend we have ever known, and the greatest champion of freedom who has ever brought help and comfort from the new world to the old."[16]

Stalin's heated confrontations with Churchill and his angry accusation that the British were afraid of fighting Germans (13 June) are frankly recounted, and Churchill's response is likewise documented. Makins was less careful about offending Russians: the reader learns five installments later, in a handsome presentation of the invasion of Europe by Anglo-American-Canadian forces on June 6, 1944, that Stalin was wrong. And a page later, we are shown the horror of the flying bombs Hitler loosed on London, in the second great blitz of the war (26 July).

We witness Victory in Europe Day, May 8, 1945, almost as a coda to the story, and here the canny Frank Bellamy may have missed one of the most dramatic scenes of the war: Churchill waving to the crowds from the Ministry of Health in Whitehall, shouting into the microphone, "God bless you all."

'I had the luck to be called upon to give the roar'

Lest works like "The Happy Warrior" be too devoted to his own persona, Churchill himself made sure that his countrymen received the thanks. He expresses that here (23 Aug.), but more eloquently perhaps in 1954 when, honored by Parliament on his eightieth birthday, he said of the British people:

> *Their will was resolute and remorseless, and as it proved, unconquerable. It fell to me to express it, and if I found the right words you must remember that I have always earned my living by my pen and by my tongue. It was a nation and race dwelling all round the globe that had the lion heart. I had the luck to be called upon to give the roar. I also hope that I sometimes suggested to the lion the right places to use his claws.*[17]

V-E Day is the end of our story. "The Happy Warrior" makes no attempt to discuss the rest of the war, perhaps because Churchill was no longer in charge. More surprisingly, but possibly because they were recent and contentious topics, there is also nothing about his 1946 "Iron Curtain" speech warning of Soviet ambitions; of his second premiership, when the vision of nuclear extinction sent him on a failed quest for peace with the Russians; or of his bittersweet postwar relations with Eisenhower over summit meetings, decolonization, and Suez. Those were recent events in 1958, and perhaps too painful; the *Eagle* was in the business of defining heroes.

What can we make of this half-century-old tribute? The story is accurately told, the figures remarkably true to life. But it is only part of the Churchill story, and should not lead the reader to think he was strictly a man of war.

Churchill concluded early in life that "the story of the human race is war," and—at least before the advent of nuclear weapons—regarded wars as recurring phenomena. Because he always urged fighting with "might and main" he is often regarded purely as a warrior. It is less well known that he tried to stop the First World War, and the Second. Some authors have even truncated his quotations to make him fit their vision of a war enthusiast. Here is one unedited quotation that makes clear his true attitude:

> *Much as war attracts me & fascinates my mind with its tremendous situations—*
> *I feel more deeply every year—& can measure the feeling here in the midst of*
> *arms—what vile & wicked folly & barbarism it all is.*[18]

Another point one draws from the narrative is more positive: for the vast majority of free peoples, what "The Happy Warrior" says is still accepted, and probably always will be. In 1995 the late William Buckley, in an unforgettable speech, gave the best rationale for this work when he said:

Mr. Churchill had struggled to diminish totalitarian rule in Europe, which however increased. He fought to save the Empire, which dissolved. He fought socialism, which prevailed. He struggled to defeat Hitler, and he won. It is not I think the significance of that victory, mighty and glorious though it was, that causes the name of Churchill to make the blood run a little faster. He subsequently spoke diffidently about his role in the war, saying that the lion was the people of England, that he had served mainly to provide the roar. But it is the roar that we hear when we pronounce his name; it is simply mistaken that battles are necessarily more important than the words that summon men to arms or who remember the call to arms. The Battle of Agincourt was long forgotten as a geopolitical event, but the words of Henry V, with Shakespeare to recall them, are imperishable in the mind, even as which side won the Battle of Gettysburg will dim from the memory of men and women who will never forget the words spoken about that battle by Abraham Lincoln. The genius of Churchill was his union of affinities of the heart and of the mind, the total fusion of animal and spiritual energy.[19]

One is left only to wonder how the Happy Warrior himself saw this comic upon its publication—for he was alive and sentient, and such things usually were brought to his attention. One may imagine him as his daughter did, sitting in his garden chair at Chartwell, strategically among the foliage, watching the butterflies as they fluttered over the buddleia he had planted for them.[20] Though he was growing old thinking he had not accomplished very much in the end, "The Happy Warrior" might have given him pause.

It was William Buckley's proposal that Churchill's words were "indispensable to the benediction of that hour," Britain's finest, whatever the glories that came before or the disappointments that came after. It is no coincidence that our view of Churchill is still more or less that of Clifford Makins and Frank Bellamy fifty years ago. For those who remember, or are willing to learn, Winston Churchill is still the Happy Warrior.

---

1   Winston S. Churchill, Woodford, Essex, 12 October 1951. Robert Rhodes James, ed. *Winston S. Churchill: His Complete Speeches 1897-1963*, vol. 8 (New York: Bowker, 1974), 8263.

2   Prof. Paul Addison, University of Edinburgh, author of *Churchill on the Home Front* (1992), in *Finest Hour* 127 (summer 2005): 6.

3   Current scholarship holds Churchill much less to blame for the Dardanelles fiasco than twentieth-century opinion; indeed, he had preferred a Baltic flanking attack, though he did go all-out for the Dardanelles once the plan was agreed on.

4   Kay Halle, *Irrepressible Churchill* (New York and Cleveland: World, 1966), 200.

5   Winston S. Churchill, *The Second World War*, vol. 6, *Triumph and Tragedy* (London: Cassell, 1954), 583.

6   Winston S. Churchill, *My Early Life: A Roving Commission* (London: Thornton Butterworth; New York: Charles Scribner's Sons, 1930), 15-57.

7   Ephesian [C.E. Bechhofer Roberts], *Winston Churchill*, 3rd ed. (London: George Newnes, 1936), 74.

8   Winston S. Churchill, *The River War*, vol. 2 (London: Longmans Green, 1899), 221.

9   Winston S. Churchill, *London to Ladysmith via Pretoria* (London: Longmans Green, 1900), 134-35.

10 Martin Gilbert, *Churchill: A Life* (London: Heinemann, 1991), 321.

11 House of Commons, 23 November 1932. Rhodes James, *Complete Speeches*, vol. 5, 5199-5200.

12 Winston S. Churchill, *Arms and the Covenant* (London: George Harrap, 1938), 465. Not in House of Commons transcripts; the passage was likely added by Churchill to his book.

13 House of Commons, 5 October 1938. Winston S. Churchill, *Blood, Sweat and Tears* (Toronto: McClelland & Stewart, 1941), 76-77.

14 Circa 1941. Sir John Colville to the author, 1985.

15 House of Commons, 11 February 1943. Rhodes James, *Complete Speeches*, vol. 7, 6752.

16 House of Commons, 17 April 1945. Rhodes James, *Complete Speeches*, vol. 7, 7141.

17 House of Commons, 30 November 1954. Rhodes James, *Complete Speeches*, vol. 8, 8608-09.

18 Churchill to his wife, 15 September 1909. In Randolph S. Churchill, *Winston S. Churchill, Companion Volume II, Part 2* (London: Heinemann, 1967), 912.

19 William F. Buckley, Jr., "Let Us Now Praise Famous Men," 12th International Churchill Conference, Boston, 27 October 1995. *Churchill Proceedings 1994-1995* (Hopkinton, N.H.: The Churchill Centre, 1998), 81-82.

20 Mary Soames, 120th Birthday Celebration, Naval and Military Club, London, 29 November 1994.

BEGINNING TODAY !

The HAPPY WARRIOR

The true life story of
SIR WINSTON CHURCHILL

WINSTON CHURCHILL WAS BORN AT BLENHEIM PALACE ON THE 30th NOVEMBER, 1874.

TOLD BY CLIFFORD MAKINS
DRAWN BY FRANK BELLAMY

YOUNG WINSTON LOVED READING...

..AND PLAYING WITH TOY SOLDIERS.

WOULD YOU LIKE TO BE A SOLDIER, BOY ?

OH YES, PAPA !

YOU SHALL, MY BOY, YOU SHALL.

WHEN HE WAS 12, WINSTON SAT FOR THE ENTRANCE EXAMINATION FOR HARROW.

THE LATIN PAPER ! OH DEAR !

WINSTON DID NOT DO VERY WELL

CHURCHILL'S LATIN IS NOT UP TO MUCH ! NEVER MIND, WE WILL PUT HIM IN THE BOTTOM FORM, AND HOPE, FOR THE BEST.

BUT WINSTON WAS VERY GOOD AT ENGLISH, WHICH HE ADORED.

WELL DONE, CHURCHILL. A SPLENDID EFFORT.

WINSTON SOON FOUND A WAY ROUND THE PROBLEM OF LATIN !

IF YOU TELL ME MY LATIN TRANSLATIONS, I WILL WRITE YOUR ENGLISH ESSAYS.

WHAT A SPLENDID IDEA !

CONTINUED

1

EAGLE 11 *October* 1957

The HAPPY WARRIOR

The true life story of
SIR WINSTON CHURCHILL

Winston Churchill was born in 1874. He went to school at Harrow, where he was only an average scholar, although he excelled at English. While stagnating in the lowest form, Churchill won a prize open to the whole school, reciting 1,200 lines of Macaulay's *Lays of Ancient Rome* . . .

**TOLD BY CLIFFORD MAKINS
DRAWN BY FRANK BELLAMY**

LARS PORSENA OF CLUSIUM BY THE NINE GODS HE SWORE !

WELL DONE, CHURCHILL ! A FIRST RATE PERFORMANCE !

WINSTON LOVED SINGING THE FAMOUS SCHOOL SONGS OF HARROW . . .

. . . AND HE WON THE PUBLIC SCHOOL CHAMPIONSHIP IN FENCING !

When Winston left Harrow, he passed into Sandhurst – after three tries ! At the end of his course, he was placed eighth out of 150. In 1895, he was gazetted to the 4th Hussars, a famous cavalry regiment stationed at Aldershot . . .

WINSTON SOON BECAME AN EXPERT HORSEMAN — LEARNING THE HARD WAY !

CHURCHILL LONGED TO SEE ACTION AND LISTENED SPELLBOUND TO THE YARNS OF HIS COMMANDER, COLONEL BRABAZON.

BARNES, THERE'S A WAR IN CUBA. WE MIGHT HAVE A LOOK AT IT. WHAT D'YOU THINK ?

I'M GAME, CHURCHILL.

SPLENDID ! WE HAVE THE COLONEL'S BLESSING, AND HERE ARE THE PAPERS FROM THE SPANISH AUTHORITIES.

IN 1895, CHURCHILL AND BARNES SAILED TO NEW YORK AND FROM THENCE TO HAVANA . . .

CUBA ! HOW EXCITING— HOW MYSTERIOUS !

WHERE ARE THE ENEMY ?

HERE, THERE AND EVERYWHERE ! IF YOU WANT TO SEE FIGHTING, YOU MUST JOIN A MOBILE COLUMN !

WINSTON JOINED A SPANISH COLUMN WHICH WAS HUNTING CUBAN REBELS . . .

AH, ACTION AT LAST !

CONTINUED

EAGLE 18 October 1957

The HAPPY WARRIOR

The true life story of
SIR WINSTON CHURCHILL

Winston Churchill – born in the year 1874 – went to Harrow School, and then on to Sandhurst, where he did well. In 1895, Churchill was gazetted to the 4th Hussars, a famous cavalry regiment, at that time stationed at Aldershot – but love of adventure and longing for action soon took Winston, together with a fellow subaltern, to Cuba, where the Spaniards were fighting a war against rebels . . .

TOLD BY CLIFFORD MAKINS
DRAWN BY FRANK BELLAMY

THE REBELS HAVE RUN DEEP INTO THE JUNGLE. WE CANNOT FOLLOW THEM THERE.

THAT WAS A PRETTY POOR SCRAP!

MAYBE – BUT IT WAS REAL – IT WAS EXCITING! DID YOU HEAR THOSE BULLETS SMITING THE TREES?

SOON AFTER, THE TWO SUBALTERNS LEFT CUBA.

GOODBYE, CUBA — HOME TO ENGLAND!

WINSTON RETURNED TO HIS REGIMENT AT ALDERSHOT...

WHAT SPLENDID NEWS!

WELCOME BACK, CHURCHILL! IN SIX MONTHS, THE REGIMENT SAILS FOR INDIA.

Winston spent six months' leave in English society and, during this period, he met many famous men of the day. Among them was General Sir Bindon Blood, hero of campaigns on the turbulent Indian frontier . . .

SIR! WHEN YOU LEAD YOUR NEXT EXPEDITION IN INDIA, I BEG YOU TO LET ME COME.

ALL RIGHT – THAT'S A PROMISE!

IN AUTUMN 1896 WINSTON'S REGIMENT SAILED TO BOMBAY

WINSTON AND HIS FRIENDS, BARNES AND BARING, SHARED A FINE BUNGALOW AT THE BANGALORE GARRISON.

HERE IS OUR HOUSE, GENTLEMEN! LET US MAKE OURSELVES AT HOME!

IN INDIA, CHURCHILL WAS A POLO FANATIC...

...AND A GREAT READER.

Later, when tribesmen rose on the North-West Frontier, Sir Bindon Blood led a force against them. Winston immediately set off to join him, both in the capacity of a soldier, and as correspondent for the Indian *Pioneer* and the British *Daily Telegraph*.

TWO THOUSAND MILES AND FIVE DAYS' TRAVEL TO THE FRONTIER. WHAT A JOURNEY!

I'LL GET THERE! GOODBYE!

SIX DAYS LATER, WINSTON REACHED THE FRONT AT THE MALAKAND PASS...

LT. CHURCHILL REPORTING TO GENERAL SIR BINDON BLOOD!

CONTINUED

3

EAGLE 25 October 1957

The HAPPY WARRIOR

The true life story of **SIR WINSTON CHURCHILL**

CONTINUED

EAGLE 1 *November* 1957

The HAPPY WARRIOR

The true life story of **SIR WINSTON CHURCHILL**

India, 1896. Lt. Winston Churchill has gone to the North-West Frontier to join the Malakand Field Force which is fighting rebel tribesmen. He joins a brigade which advances into the Mamund Valley and soon finds himself engaged in a desperate action with a small company of men. Under withering fire, the company retreats down a hill with its wounded . . .

TOLD BY CLIFFORD MAKINS
DRAWN BY FRANK BELLAMY

PRESS ON WITH THE WOUNDED. I'LL KEEP THE SAVAGES AT BAY!

AIEE!

WINSTON ALONE FACED THE FIERCE PATHAN TRIBESMEN.

MISSED, MY FINE FRIEND! NOW YOU ARE FOR IT!

THE TRIBESMAN FELL BEHIND A ROCK!

STILL MORE OF THEM! I MUST MAKE FOR COVER!

AS WINSTON DASHES OVER THE ROCKS, THE BULLETS WHINE AROUND HIM.

SPLENDID WORK!

TO THE BOTTOM OF THE HILL WITH THE WOUNDED! HURRY!

WINSTON FIRED SHOT AFTER SHOT AS THE COMPANY STRUGGLED DOWN THE HILL.

COURAGE, MEN! WE'RE NEARLY THERE!

CONTINUED

EAGLE 8 November 1957

The HAPPY WARRIOR

The true life story of
SIR WINSTON CHURCHILL

In 1896, Lt. Winston Churchill is on the Indian North-West Frontier with the Malakand Field Force which is fighting rebel tribesmen. Winston takes part in a spirited action in the Mamund Valley. His company is hard pressed and suffers heavy casualties, but with great dash and courage Winston conducts a fighting retreat to the British lines.

TOLD BY CLIFFORD MAKINS
DRAWN BY FRANK BELLAMY

HURRAH! WE'VE MADE THE LINES.

WINSTON BROUGHT THE COMPANY SAFELY HOME!

BUT THE FRENZIED TRIBESMEN SURGED ON!

FIRE!

THEY'RE ON THE RUN!

THE TRIBESMEN'S MAD RUSH WAS HALTED JUST IN TIME. THEY FLED IN DISORDER.

PHEW! THAT WAS WARM WORK!

SPLENDID FELLOW!

WINSTON RETURNS TO BANGALORE.

WINSTON'S BACK!

HERE HE COMES!

YOU'VE CERTAINLY HAD A FIRST RATE WAR, WINSTON!

I HAVE — AND NOW I'M GOING TO WRITE A BOOK ABOUT IT!

AND SO THE TIRELESS WINSTON WROTE A BOOK ABOUT HIS ADVENTURES CALLED 'THE MALAKAND FIELD FORCE'.

When Winston's book was published it was well received and praised by the Prince of Wales and the Prime Minister, Lord Salisbury. But Winston craved action again. On leave in England, he had news that Sir Herbert Kitchener's army was advancing against the Dervishes in the Sudan.

I WANT TO FIGHT IN THE SUDAN CAMPAIGN. DO YOU THINK THE PRIME MINISTER WOULD PUT IN A WORD FOR ME?

CERTAINLY! I'LL ASK HIM RIGHT AWAY.

LATER...

THE PRIME MINISTER HAS SENT A WIRE TO KITCHENER.

WONDERFUL!

BUT THE NEXT DAY...

BAD NEWS, WINSTON— KITCHENER HAS WIRED BACK 'NO'. HE HAS ALL THE OFFICERS HE REQUIRES.

THAT'S A BLOW! BUT I REFUSE TO BE BEATEN!

CONTINUED

The Nile

*After six miles hard riding he sights
the allied armies from a hill...*

EAGLE 15 November 1957

The HAPPY WARRIOR

The true life story of
SIR WINSTON CHURCHILL

After fighting on the Indian North-West Frontier, Lt. Winston Churchill returns to England on leave. He tries to attach himself to Sir Herbert Kitchener's army which is marching against the Dervishes in the Sudan. But although the Prime Minister puts in a word for Winston, Kitchener wires his refusal. Winston talks with his friend, Sir Schomberg M'Donnell...

TOLD BY CLIFFORD MAKINS
DRAWN BY FRANK BELLAMY

I MUST GET TO THE SUDAN! I'LL ASK LADY ST. HELIER. SHE'S A GREAT FRIEND OF THE ADJUTANT-GENERAL, SIR EVELYN WOOD!

GOOD FOR YOU, WINSTON!

WINSTON WASTED NO TIME...

I ADMIRE YOUR SPIRIT, WINSTON. I WILL SPEAK TO THE ADJUTANT GENERAL MYSELF.

MA'AM, I AM GREATLY OBLIGED TO YOU.

A FEW DAYS LATER...

A LETTER FROM THE WAR OFFICE! HURRAH! I'VE BEEN POSTED TO EGYPT. I SHALL JUST BE IN TIME FOR THE BATTLE!

GOODBYE, MOTHER!

THE NEXT DAY, WINSTON'S MOTHER WAVED HIM GOODBYE!

SIX DAYS LATER, HE JOINED THE 21st LANCERS IN CAIRO...

WELL, MR CHURCHILL—YOU MUST HAVE PULLED A FEW STRINGS TO GET HERE!

YES, SIR.

I WONDER WHAT KITCHENER THINKS OF THIS!

AUGUST 27th, 1898. KITCHENER'S ARMIES SWARMED ACROSS THE NILE...

THAT'S THE LOT —ALL SAFELY ACROSS.

AND STILL NO SIGN OF THE ENEMY.

WE'RE ON THE MOVE! OUR SQUADRON WILL SUPPORT THE ADVANCED PATROLS.

ALL RIGHT, MEN —HERE WE GO!

MR CHURCHILL! THE ENEMY IS SEVEN MILES AWAY AND ADVANCING—RIDE AT ONCE TO KITCHENER AND TELL HIM!

I'M OFF, SIR!

CONTINUED

EAGLE 22 *November* 1957

The HAPPY WARRIOR

The true life story of
SIR WINSTON CHURCHILL

1898. Lt. Winston Churchill has been attached to the 21st Lancers for the Sudan Campaign where British and Egyptian armies, under Sir Herbert Kitchener, are fighting the Dervishes. On the eve of the Battle of Omdurman, Winston gallops to the Commander-in-Chief to report the enemy's positions. After six miles hard riding he sights the allied armies from a hill . . .

TOLD BY CLIFFORD MAKINS
DRAWN BY FRANK BELLAMY

WHAT A SPLENDID SIGHT ! AH, THERE IS KITCHENER — RIDING AT THE HEAD !

SIR, I AM REPORTING FROM THE 21st LANCERS. THE ENEMY IS ABOUT SEVEN MILES AWAY AND ADVANCING STEADILY.

PHEW ! I HOPE MY INFORMATION IS CORRECT ! NOW I MUST REJOIN MY SQUADRON !

I HAVE INFORMED KITCHENER OF THE SITUATION.

GOOD ! BUT NOW THE DERVISH ADVANCE HAS STOPPED. WE WILL HAVE OUR BATTLE TOMORROW !

NEXT DAY THE TWO ARMIES CLASHED . . .

THE BATTLE IS ON. SOON IT WILL BE OUR TURN.

THE ENEMY'S ATTACK HAS BEEN REPULSED.

NOW WE MUST KEEP THEM ON THE RUN. PREPARE TO ADVANCE.

THE 21st LANCERS CHARGED INTO BATTLE.

NOW THEN !

NO SWORD FOR ME ! THE PISTOL IS MY BEST FRIEND !

IT'S DEATH OR GLORY NOW !

CONTINUED

9

EAGLE 29 *November* 1957

The HAPPY WARRIOR

The true life story of
SIR WINSTON CHURCHILL

CONTINUED

EAGLE 6 *December* 1957

The HAPPY WARRIOR

The true life story of
SIR WINSTON CHURCHILL

On the great desert plain of the Nile, the Battle of Omdurman is being fought. The Dervish hordes have been repelled by intense fire from the British-Egyptian armies, under Sir Herbert Kitchener. Lt. Winston Churchill, with the 21st Lancers, leads his troop in a rousing Cavalry charge. As the troop reforms, a savage bursts into the ranks with a spear and rushes straight towards Winston.

TOLD BY CLIFFORD MAKINS
DRAWN BY FRANK BELLAMY

JUST IN TIME — AND THAT WAS MY LAST SHOT!

WHAT CASUALTIES HAVE WE SUFFERED, SERGEANT?

FOUR MEN MISSING, SIR, AND SEVERAL OTHERS WOUNDED. NOT SO BAD!

WE MUST PREPARE TO CHARGE AGAIN ON COMMAND — AH, HERE COMES THE SQUADRON LEADER!

RIDE BACK TO THE ENEMY'S FLANK AND HALT! WE'LL TREAT THEM TO SOME GUN-FIRE NOW.

RIGHT, SIR! FORWARD!

DISMOUNT — AND GET INTO LINE!

KEEP UP YOUR FIRE! THEY'RE RETREATING!

IT'S ALL OVER, SERGEANT. THE BATTLE IS OURS!

YES, SIR. THAT WAS QUITE A SCRAP!

THE BATTLE OF OMDURMAN WAS OVER. WINSTON SAILED BACK UP THE NILE TO CAIRO.

WELL, THAT WAS A QUICK WAR AND NO MISTAKE.

GOOD OLD WINSTON — ESCAPED WITHOUT A SCRATCH AS USUAL!

HERE COMES WINSTON BACK FROM THE WARS!

BRAVO!

AND *NOW* WHAT ARE YOU GOING TO DO, WINSTON?

WRITE ANOTHER BOOK, WIN THE INDIAN POLO TOURNAMENT, GO INTO POLITICS AND FIGHT IN ANY WAR THAT COMES ALONG!

CONTINUED

EAGLE 13 December 1957

The HAPPY WARRIOR

The true life story of
SIR WINSTON CHURCHILL

Attached to the 21st Lancers in the Sudan, Lt. Winston Churchill fights in the battle of Omdurman against the Dervishes, and distinguishes himself in an historic cavalry charge on the banks of the Nile. Then, the war won, he returns to London, where he is welcomed in society.

TOLD BY CLIFFORD MAKINS
DRAWN BY FRANK BELLAMY

GOODBYE! WHEN SHALL WE SEE YOU AGAIN?

NEXT SPRING I HOPE. AFTER THE POLO TOURNAMENT. I SHALL LEAVE THE ARMY AND LIVE IN LONDON.

Winston went to India and helped his regiment win the Polo Tournament of 1899. Resigning his commission, he came home to England, where, after contesting Oldham unsuccessfully for the Tories, he settled down to write his book 'The River War'. But then . . .

MR OLIVER BORTHWICK OF THE MORNING POST TO SEE YOU, SIR.

THANK YOU. SHOW HIM IN.

OLIVER!

WINSTON! THE BOER REPUBLICS HAVE ISSUED AN ULTIMATUM TO OUR FORCES IN SOUTH AFRICA. WAR IS IMMINENT. WILL YOU ACT AS PRINCIPAL WAR CORRESPONDENT FOR THE MORNING POST?

WHEN DO I START?

IMMEDIATELY! YOU SAIL ON THE NEXT BOAT!

I WISH THIS SHIP WOULD GET A MOVE ON. BY THE TIME WE REACH THE CAPE THE WAR WILL BE OVER!

THE BOERS ARE BESIEGING LADYSMITH AND MAFEKING IN NATAL PROVINCE.

THAT'S THE PLACE FOR ME!

WINSTON WENT TO THE FRONT LINE AT ESTCOURT IN NATAL AND MET AN OLD FRIEND . . .

CHURCHILL!

HALDANE!

I'M TAKING AN ARMOURED TRAIN ON RECONNAISSANCE! CARE TO COME ALONG?

LIKE A SHOT!

HERE WE ARE, WINSTON. HOP IN!

I THINK WE SHOULD PUT ON A SHOW FOR YOU, WINSTON!

I HOPE SO. MUSTN'T DISAPPOINT THE READERS OF THE MORNING POST!

CONTINUED

South Africa

*Outside Pretoria, Winston jumped a train…
and spent the day hiding in a wood.*

EAGLE 20 *December* 1957

The HAPPY WARRIOR

The true life story of
SIR WINSTON CHURCHILL

War has broken out between the British and the Boers in South Africa. Lt. Winston Churchill has hurried to the front as principal war correspondent of the Morning Post. At Estcourt, in Natal, he meets a friend, Captain Haldane, and accompanies him on reconnaissance in an armoured train . . .

TOLD BY CLIFFORD MAKINS
DRAWN BY FRANK BELLAMY

WE'LL STOP HERE A MOMENT, WINSTON, AND TELEGRAPH OUR POSITION TO HEADQUARTERS.

RIGHT!

LOOK, HALDANE! ON THE HILL!

THE HILL BEHIND THE TRAIN WAS SWARMING WITH ENEMY TROOPS!

IT'S THE BOERS! THEY'RE CUTTING US OFF. FULL STEAM BACK TO H.Q., OR WE SHALL LOSE TROOPS, TRAIN AND ALL!

WE'RE PASSING THE BOERS NOW!

WAIT FOR IT!

FIRE!

THE TRAIN GOT THE FULL FURY OF THE ENEMY FIRE.

HALDANE! I THINK WE ... AH!

THE TRAIN STOPPED — VIOLENTLY!

IF YOUR CHAPS KEEP FIRING, I'LL NIP OUT AND SEE WHAT'S HAPPENED TO THE TRAIN!

RIGHT, CHURCHILL!

GOOD LORD — WHAT A MESS!

CONTINUED

14

EAGLE 27 December 1957

The HAPPY WARRIOR

The true life story of
SIR WINSTON CHURCHILL

Winston Churchill has gone to South Africa as correspondent for the Morning Post to report the war between Britain and the Boer Republics. He goes on reconnaissance with an armoured train in Natal Province. Without warning, the train is attacked by Boers and derailed. Winston, braving enemy fire, runs towards the head of the train . . .

TOLD BY CLIFFORD MAKINS
DRAWN BY FRANK BELLAMY

WE MUST CLEAR THE LINE AND GET THE TRAIN ON THE MOVE — AH, THERE'S THE ENGINE DRIVER!

HE'S RUNNING AWAY! HI! COME BACK HERE!

HANDS OFF! LET ME GO! I'M NOT RISKING MY LIFE ANY MORE.

YOU'RE DOING A GREAT JOB! BACK YOU GO — AND WAIT FOR ORDERS.

WINSTON PERSUADED THE ENGINE DRIVER TO RETURN TO HIS CAB.

STAND CLEAR! I'M GOING TO DRIVE THE ENGINE FULL TILT TO TRY TO CLEAR THE LINE!

QUICK, DRIVER! LET IT RIP!

THE ENGINE PUSHED THE WRECKAGE FROM THE LINE.

ALL ABOARD — QUICK AS YOU CAN!

THERE'S THE BRIDGE. ONCE ACROSS THE GORGE WE CAN TAKE STOCK OF THE SITUATION.

STOP THE TRAIN! THE REST OF THE TROOP ARE FALLING BEHIND. I'LL GO BACK AND HURRY THEM ON.

AH! THERE THEY ARE.

NO! YE GODS — IT'S THE BOERS!

TO BE CONTINUED

EAGLE 3 *January* 1958

The HAPPY WARRIOR

The true life story of **SIR WINSTON CHURCHILL**

November, 1899. The Boer War has broken out in South Africa and Lt. Winston Churchill is reporting the campaign for the Morning Post. At the front, in Natal Province, Winston goes on reconnaissance in an armoured train which is ambushed by the Boers, and derailed. Winston takes charge of the operations and frees the engine from the wreckage. He then leaves the engine and goes to rally the British soldiers trailing behind, but is trapped by the Boers himself.

TOLD BY CLIFFORD MAKINS
DRAWN BY FRANK BELLAMY

THE BOERS — I'M TRAPPED!

DESPERATELY, WINSTON SCRAMBLED UP THE BANK AT THE SIDE OF THE TRACK...

I'VE SHAKEN THEM OFF BUT I CAN'T STAY HERE! THE RIVER'S NOT FAR AWAY — I'LL MAKE A DASH FOR IT.

BUT WHEN WINSTON STOOD UP...
HALT! STAY WHERE YOU ARE!
I'VE NO OPTION. PERHAPS I CAN GET HIM BEFORE HE GETS ME!

MY PISTOL — IT'S GONE!

NOTHING TO DO BUT SURRENDER.

CROSS THE LINE — QUICKLY!

THERE ARE THE REST OF YOUR FRIENDS — ALL PRISONERS!

TAKE THIS MAN AND STAND HIM APART FROM THE OTHERS. WE'LL DEAL WITH HIM IN A MOMENT!

WAR CORRESPONDENTS WHO TAKE PART IN THE FIGHT ARE USUALLY SHOT.

THIS LOOKS LIKE THE END FOR ME!

TO BE CONTINUED

EAGLE 10 *January* 1958

The HAPPY WARRIOR

The true life story of
SIR WINSTON CHURCHILL

Winston Churchill, aged 25, and principal war correspondent of the Morning Post, is reporting the Boer War in South Africa. He goes on re-connaissance with a party of troops in an armoured train and, after taking an active part in a fierce fight, is taken prisoner. He is placed apart from the other prisoners and stands in the pouring rain, expecting to be shot!

TOLD BY CLIFFORD MAKINS
DRAWN BY FRANK BELLAMY

CHEER UP! IF WE DECIDE TO SHOOT YOU WE'LL GIVE YOU A DECENT BURIAL!

THANKS VERY MUCH!

AH, THEY'VE MADE THEIR DECISION. YOU'LL KNOW YOUR FATE IN A MINUTE.

YOU CAN COME ALONG WITH THE OTHER PRISONERS, CHURCHILL. WE DON'T CATCH THE SON OF A LORD EVERY DAY!

COME ON! STEP IT OUT, THERE — ONLY ANOTHER FIFTY MILES TO GO!

EVENTUALLY WINSTON ARRIVED AT THE PRISON-CAMP FOR OFFICERS IN PRETORIA.

WELL HERE WE ARE — PRISON AT LAST!

THANK GOODNESS — I'M DEAD BEAT!

ONE MONTH LATER.

I'M GOING TO GET OUT OF THIS PLACE EVEN IF I DIE IN THE ATTEMPT!

IT'S CERTAINLY OUR DUTY TO ESCAPE IF WE CAN.

MY MIND'S MADE UP. I SHALL TRY TO GIVE THE SENTRIES THE SLIP AND JUMP OVER THE WALL — TONIGHT!

AND THAT EVENING, IN CIVILIAN CLOTHING, WINSTON AWAITED HIS OPPORTUNITY...

IF ONLY THOSE TWO SENTRIES WOULD HAVE A CHAT TOGETHER, I'D STAND A CHANCE!

GOOD! NOW'S THE TIME!

AS THE SENTRIES ENJOYED A SMOKE WINSTON SLIPPED OVER THE FENCE.

DONE IT!

TO BE CONTINUED

EAGLE 17 *January* 1958

The HAPPY WARRIOR

The true life story of
SIR WINSTON CHURCHILL

While reporting the Boer War in South Africa, Lt. Winston Churchill takes part in a reconnaissance on an armoured train. He distinguishes himself, but is captured and taken to an officers' prison camp at Pretoria. Determined to escape, he makes his attempt in bright moonlight and scales the wall of the prison compound without being seen . . .

TOLD BY CLIFFORD MAKINS
DRAWN BY FRANK BELLAMY

I'M FREE —AND NO SOUND OF AN ALARM.

ANOTHER SENTRY! WELL, CAN'T TURN BACK NOW—MUST RISK IT!

RIGHT UNDER HIS NOSE —AND NOT A CHALLENGE!

Outside Pretoria, Winston jumped a train. At daybreak he left the train and spent the day hiding in a wood. At night he waited for another train, but none came. In despair, he left the railway line . . .

PHEW! THE GOING'S TOUGH! I'M JUST ABOUT ALL IN!

HOURS LATER . . .

A COAL MINE — I'LL STOP HERE AND TRY TO BLUFF MY WAY THROUGH.

WHO IS IT? WHAT DO YOU WANT?

I NEED HELP. I'VE HAD AN ACCIDENT.

I'VE FALLEN OFF A TRAIN AND I THINK I'VE DISLOCATED MY SHOULDER.

COME IN THEN.

NOW WHO ARE YOU AND WHERE DO YOU COME FROM? AND I'D LIKE TO KNOW THE TRUTH!

RIGHT, I WILL TELL YOU THE TRUTH. I AM WINSTON CHURCHILL, WAR-CORRESPONDENT OF THE MORNING POST. LAST NIGHT I ESCAPED FROM PRETORIA AND I AM MAKING MY WAY TO THE FRONTIER.

DON'T MOVE AND KEEP QUIET!

NOW I'M DONE FOR!

I'M GLAD TO KNOW YOU MR CHURCHILL. THANK GOD YOU STUMBLED ACROSS THIS PLACE. WE ARE ALL BRITISH HERE AND WILL SEE YOU THROUGH!

TO BE CONTINUED

EAGLE 24 January 1958

The HAPPY WARRIOR

The true life story of
SIR WINSTON CHURCHILL

Lt. Winston Churchill, war correspondent of the Morning Post, is taken prisoner while reporting the Boer War in South Africa. He escapes from the prison camp at Pretoria and after hours of wandering over the veldt seeks shelter at a coal mine. Luckily, the manager is an Englishman and promises to help Winston on his way.

TOLD BY CLIFFORD MAKINS
DRAWN BY FRANK BELLAMY

THE BOERS ARE LOOKING EVERYWHERE FOR YOU. THEY WERE HERE THIS AFTERNOON. BUT DON'T WORRY — SIT DOWN AND I'LL GET YOU SOME FOOD.

THANK YOU — I'M FAMISHED!

LATER...

FINISHED YOUR MEAL? GOOD! COME ON, MR CHURCHILL, I'VE SPOKEN TO THE MEN AND WE'RE GOING TO HIDE YOU DOWN THE PIT.

HERE ARE SOME CANDLES. YOU'LL BE QUITE SAFE HERE, BUT DON'T MOVE WHATEVER HAPPENS. WE WON'T FORGET YOU!

THIS IS HARDLY HOME FROM HOME BUT IT'S BETTER THAN PRISON. I'LL SOON BE OUT OF HERE, PLEASE GOD, AND BACK IN THE FRAY AGAIN.

After six days in the mine, while Boers hunted him overhead, Winston was stowed away on a goods train bound for Portuguese East Africa. Soon he reached his goal and strolled through the streets of Lourenço Marques.

THE BRITISH CONSULATE — WHAT A BLESSED SIGHT!

I WANT TO SEE THE CONSUL.

BE OFF WITH YOU! IF YOU HAVE ANY BUSINESS WITH THE CONSUL CALL TOMORROW MORNING AT NINE!

YOU GO TO BLAZES! I WANT TO SEE THE CONSUL RIGHT AWAY! RIGHT NOW!

WHAT ON EARTH IS THE MATTER? I AM THE CONSUL.

AND I AM WINSTON CHURCHILL — ESCAPED FROM THE BOERS!

WINSTON CHURCHILL! WELCOME, MY DEAR CHAP — YOU'RE A HERO!

Winston's escape made him famous throughout the world. Returning to the Army he served as Lieutenant with the South African Light Horse until the following year when Pretoria was captured.

WELL, CHURCHILL, THE WAR'S NEARLY OVER. WHAT ARE YOUR PLANS NOW?

I'VE RESIGNED MY COMMISSION AND AM RETURNING TO ENGLAND. I HEAR THERE'S A GENERAL ELECTION IN THE OFFING.

TO BE CONTINUED

The Admiralty
and
The First World War

...his special job was to help with the planning of the Gallipoli campaign. But it was too late.

EAGLE 28 *February* 1958

The HAPPY WARRIOR

The true life story of **SIR WINSTON CHURCHILL**

France, 1916. Lt. Colonel Churchill of 6th Royal Scots Fusiliers has lost his command because of his battalion's amalgamation with another unit. He is urged to leave the army and to return to the home front where his marked abilities may be used, once again, to help run the war.

TOLD BY CLIFFORD MAKINS
DRAWN BY FRANK BELLAMY

GOODBYE, CHURCHILL. WE ALL HOPE THAT YOU'LL RETURN TO WESTMINSTER AT THE EARLIEST OPPORTUNITY.

Churchill left the army and returned home to the political scene. In 1917 he was appointed Minister of Munitions to speed the flow of arms to the British Expeditionary Force.

THIS IS THE CRUCIAL STAGE OF THE WAR. WE MUST HAVE MORE TANKS, GUNS, SHELLS AND BULLETS — MORE OF EVERYTHING!

August 1918. The tide turned and the Germans retreated everywhere. British tanks, the evolution of which Churchill had encouraged, played a vital part in the Allied advance.

11 a.m. NOVEMBER 11th, 1918!

ARMISTICE!

LONDON. CHURCHILL LOOKED DOWN ON THE CROWDS.

WE'VE WON THE WAR!

PEACE! IT'S PEACE!

YES, WE'VE WON THE WAR ALL RIGHT! AND NOW WE MUST WIN THE PEACE!

TROUBLED YEARS FOLLOWED THE WAR AND CHURCHILL'S FORTUNES ROSE AND FELL...

1922 GENERAL ELECTION

I'VE LOST MY SEAT, MY PARTY AND MY APPENDIX!

1924 BACK AGAIN! CHANCELLOR OF THE EXCHEQUER

1926 GENERAL STRIKE WORKERS UNITE

NO TRAINS, BUSES, NEWSPAPERS! AND ALL THE WORKERS HAVE DOWNED TOOLS!

1929 GENERAL ELECTION AND FALL OF THE GOVERNMENT

LABOUR BACK IN POWER AGAIN! WHAT WILL YOU DO NOW, CHURCHILL?

KEEP THE OPPOSITION BENCHES WARM — AND BIDE MY TIME!

TO BE CONTINUED

EAGLE 7 March 1958

The HAPPY WARRIOR

The true life story of
SIR WINSTON CHURCHILL

England, 1929. With the fall of the Conservative Government, Winston Churchill loses his office as Chancellor of the Exchequer. But his constituents have been faithful and he still keeps his seat in the House of Commons.

TOLD BY CLIFFORD MAKINS
DRAWN BY FRANK BELLAMY

WITH LABOUR IN POWER, CHURCHILL, THE COUNTRY WILL GO FROM STRENGTH TO STRENGTH!

I VERY MUCH DOUBT IT!

The Labour Government did not last long. In the midst of the world economic crisis of 1931 a coalition government was formed, but Churchill was not invited to join it.

CHURCHILL WAS AN INDUSTRIOUS WORKER AT HIS HOME, CHARTWELL,

AND A LONE WARNING VOICE AT WESTMINSTER.

THE DEMAND IS THAT GERMANY SHOULD BE ALLOWED TO REARM... DO NOT LET US DELUDE OURSELVES!

THREE YEARS LATER IN BERLIN...

HEIL HITLER!

HEIL HITLER!

OUR GLORIOUS FATHERLAND WILL TAKE ITS RIGHTFUL PLACE AT THE HEAD OF ALL NATIONS. WE WILL CONQUER EUROPE, ASIA, THE WORLD! THE HOUR IS AT HAND!

MARCH, 1936. GERMAN TROOPS RE-OCCUPY THE RHINELAND.

MARCH, 1938. INVASION OF AUSTRIA. HITLER ENTERS VIENNA.

MARCH, 1939. GERMAN CHANCELLERY, BERLIN.

AUSTRIA IS OURS, CZECHOSLOVAKIA IS OURS! NOW FOR POLAND, FRANCE AND ENGLAND!

BEWARE OF ENGLAND, FUEHRER.

ENGLAND, FIELD-MARSHAL KEITEL, HAS NO STOMACH FOR A FIGHT. YOU WILL SEE!

AUGUST, 1939. GENERAL IRONSIDE COMES FROM POLAND TO VISIT CHURCHILL.

A GERMAN INVASION IS EXPECTED HOURLY IN POLAND, BUT ARMY MORALE IS HIGH.

I FEAR THE WORST!

DAWN, SEPTEMBER 1st. VICIOUS AIR ATTACKS MARK THE...

GERMAN INVASION OF POLAND

BOMBING RAIDS
FIVE
MASS ATTACK

AFTERNOON, SEPTEMBER 1st. PRIME MINISTER CHAMBERLAIN SENDS FOR CHURCHILL.

WAR IS IMMINENT, WINSTON. I PROPOSE TO FORM A WAR CABINET IMMEDIATELY AND I WANT YOU TO JOIN IT.

TO BE CONTINUED

Dunkirk

The vast armada of little ships
set sail across the Channel.

EAGLE 14 March 1958

The HAPPY WARRIOR

The true life story of
SIR WINSTON CHURCHILL

1st September, 1939. After weeks of mounting tension throughout Europe, Germany invades Poland, whom Britain and France are solemnly pledged to help with all their might. War is imminent. Prime Minister Neville Chamberlain calls Winston Churchill to No. 10 Downing Street and invites him to join the War Cabinet.

TOLD BY CLIFFORD MAKINS
DRAWN BY FRANK BELLAMY

PRIME MINISTER, I WILL GIVE YOU ALL THE SUPPORT WITHIN MY POWER.

I MUST TELL YOU THAT WE ARE NOW AT WAR WITH GERMANY...

BBC

11·15 a.m. SEPTEMBER 3rd, 1939.

THE AIR RAID SIRENS — THERE THEY GO!

VERY PROMPT. TRUST THE GERMANS TO WASTE NO TIME!

Churchill returned as First Lord of the Admiralty to the very room he had quitted 25 years ago. He vigorously prosecuted the war at sea. But after the quick collapse of Poland, the Western Front was quiet. This period was known as the 'phoney' war. Then in the spring of 1940.

GERMAN CHANCELLERY, BERLIN.

THE TIME HAS COME TO WIN THE WAR IN THE WEST. THIS WILL BE DONE BY STRIKING TWO MORTAL BLOWS AT THE ENEMY...

APRIL 9th, 1940. GERMAN INVASION OF DENMARK AND NORWAY. THE GERMAN AND BRITISH NAVIES CLASH AT NARVIK.

THE GERMANS SUFFERED.....

... AND SO DID THE BRITISH.

MORTALLY WOUNDED, CAPTAIN WARBURTON-LEE IN H.M.S. HARDY ISSUES HIS LAST COMMANDS.

SIGNAL FLOTILLA— 'CONTINUE TO ENGAGE THE ENEMY'!

The Norway campaign went badly for Britain. Chamberlain faced great hostility in the House.

THE GREAT BLOW!
MAY 10th, 1940. GERMANY ATTACKS ON THE WESTERN FRONT.

HOLLAND AND BELGIUM INVADED!

TO BE CONTINUED

EAGLE 28 March 1958

The HAPPY WARRIOR

The true life story of
SIR WINSTON CHURCHILL

May, 1940. Following the German attack on the Western Front, Winston Churchill becomes Prime Minister. As soon as he takes office, the mighty German army turns its full force against France and breaks the line at Sedan. The French Prime Minister calls Churchill on the telephone from Paris to say that the battle is all but lost.

TOLD BY CLIFFORD MAKINS
DRAWN BY FRANK BELLAMY

I MUST FLY TO PARIS! GENERALS DILL AND ISMAY SHALL GO WITH ME!

LE BOURGET AIRFIELD, PARIS...

WELL, HERE WE ARE!

PRAY GOD IT'S NOT TOO LATE!

QUAI D'ORSAY. FRENCH FOREIGN OFFICE.

HERE COMES WINSTON CHURCHILL.

WHAT HELP CAN HE BE TO FRANCE!

GENERAL GAMELIN, WILL YOU EXPLAIN THE SITUATION AT THE FRONT.

THE GERMANS HAVE BROKEN THROUGH NORTH AND SOUTH OF SEDAN ON A FRONT OF FIFTY MILES. THEY ARE RUSHING ON AT INCREDIBLE SPEED. OUR ARMIES ARE HOPELESSLY SHATTERED!

IMPOSSIBLE! WHAT ABOUT YOUR RESERVES? OU EST LA MASSE DE MANOEUVRE?

AUCUNE! —THERE IS NONE.

BACK IN LONDON THE FOLLOWING DAY...

GERMAN PANZER DIVISIONS ARE RAGING THROUGH FRANCE. THE BRITISH EXPEDITIONARY FORCE IS IN GRAVE PERIL. A LARGE SCALE EVACUATION MAY BE NECESSARY.

The Dutch army is shattered. Soon the Belgians surrender. The B.E.F., commanded by Lord Gort, fights a magnificent retreat to the sea. Meanwhile, Hitler exults in Berlin.

FUEHRER! GLORIOUS NEWS! THE FRENCH ARE CUT TO PIECES AND SOON THE BRITISH WILL BE HURLED INTO THE SEA!

VICTORY! VICTORY FOR THE FATHERLAND!

HEIL, HITLER!

WITH THE B.E.F. BEFORE DUNKIRK...

COME ON, LADS! FIRE OFF THE LOT AT THE BLIGHTERS, THEN WE'LL GO TO THE SEASIDE FOR THE DAY!

COR BLIMEY!

A QUIET LITTLE SPOT CALLED— DUNKIRK!

WE MUST MOVE HEAVEN AND EARTH TO EVACUATE THE ARMY FROM DUNKIRK. WE MUST SEND LIFEBOATS, DINGHIES, TRAWLERS, YACHTS — EVERYTHING AND ANYTHING THAT WILL FLOAT!

THE VAST ARMADA OF LITTLE SHIPS SET SAIL ACROSS THE CHANNEL.

WHATEVER HAPPENS AT DUNKIRK, WE SHALL FIGHT ON!

TO BE CONTINUED.

EAGLE 4 *April* 1958

The HAPPY WARRIOR

The true life story of
SIR WINSTON CHURCHILL

May, 1940. The fate of France is in the balance! German armoured columns are racing through the country. Everywhere the allied armies are in retreat. The British Expeditionary Force has fought its way to the sea. In Britain, Prime Minister Churchill is now securely at the helm. Then a great armada of little ships sails from our shores to evacuate the British Army from Dunkirk.

TOLD BY CLIFFORD MAKINS
DRAWN BY FRANK BELLAMY

THE BEACHES OF DUNKIRK, MAY 30th, 1940

ALL ABOARD! ANY MORE FOR THE SKYLARK!

HERE COMES JERRY AGAIN!

YOU ALL RIGHT, SKIPPER?

NO, I'M DONE FOR! — NEVER MIND ME. GET THE LADS ON BOARD AND GET THEM HOME.

MIDNIGHT, JUNE 4th. THE FINAL PHASE. BRITISH REARGUARD IS EMBARKED.

THAT SAME DAY. HOUSE OF COMMONS.

WE SHALL DEFEND OUR ISLAND, WHATEVER THE COST MAY BE, WE SHALL FIGHT ON THE BEACHES, WE SHALL FIGHT ON THE LANDING GROUNDS, WE SHALL FIGHT IN THE FIELDS AND IN THE STREETS, WE SHALL FIGHT IN THE HILLS; WE SHALL NEVER SURRENDER!

I MUST FLY TO FRANCE AGAIN WITH SIR JOHN DILL.

IN FRANCE, RESISTANCE WAS ALMOST AT AN END.

ALLIED SUPREME WAR COUNCIL MEETS NEAR ORLEANS.

THERE IS NOTHING TO PREVENT THE ENEMY REACHING PARIS. OUR LAST LINE HAS BEEN BREACHED. THERE ARE NO RESERVES. C'EST LA DISLOCATION — THE BREAK UP!

THEY ARE BEATEN. THEY HAVE NO WILL TO RESIST.

THE GERMANS HAVE 100 DIVISIONS TO INVADE ENGLAND. WHAT WILL YOU DO WHEN THEY SWARM ACROSS THE CHANNEL?

DROWN AS MANY AS POSSIBLE — AND AS FOR THE OTHERS, WHEN THEY CRAWL ASHORE WE WILL FRAPPER SUR LA TÊTE!

TO BE CONTINUED.

EAGLE 11 *April* 1958

The HAPPY WARRIOR

The true life story of **SIR WINSTON CHURCHILL**

June, 1940. The German blitzkrieg on the Western Front has forced Holland and Belgium to surrender and shattered the French Army. The British Expeditionary Force has been evacuated from Dunkirk by thousands of little ships plying the Channel. Winston Churchill repeatedly crosses to France to inspire the French government to fight on. But at a meeting of the Allied War Council near Orleans, the French are ready to surrender.

TOLD BY CLIFFORD MAKINS
DRAWN BY FRANK BELLAMY

GOODBYE! THIS IS A DARK HOUR BUT I AM SURE WE WILL TRIUMPH IN THE END. EVEN IF FRANCE IS OCCUPIED WE WILL STILL WIN THE WAR.

WE SHALL SEE!

POOR CHURCHILL! IN A FEW WEEK'S TIME ENGLAND'S NECK WILL BE WRUNG LIKE A CHICKEN!

On 14th June, the Germans occupied Paris. M. Reynaud, the French Prime Minister, resigned and was succeeded by the aged Marshal Petain who made peace with Adolf Hitler.

IN LONDON...

WELL, THAT'S THAT! THE BATTLE OF FRANCE IS OVER — NOW FOR THE BATTLE OF BRITAIN!

WINSTON, YOU MUST SPEAK TO THE NATION AGAIN — WITHOUT DELAY.

HITLER KNOWS THAT HE WILL HAVE TO BREAK US IN THIS ISLAND OR LOSE THE WAR ... LET US, THEREFORE, BRACE OURSELVES TO OUR DUTIES AND SO BEAR OURSELVES THAT IF THE BRITISH EMPIRE AND ITS COMMONWEALTH LAST FOR A 1,000 YEARS, MEN WILL STILL SAY *"THIS WAS THEIR FINEST HOUR"*!

MEANWHILE, THE NAZIS REJOICED...

FUEHRER, WITH OUR BASES IN FRANCE THE LUFTWAFFE WILL SHOOT THE R.A.F. FROM THE SKIES!

AND THEN THE INVASION OF ENGLAND! NOTHING CAN STOP US NOW!

IN JULY, THE BATTLE OF BRITAIN BEGAN IN EARNEST. GREAT WAVES OF GERMAN BOMBERS WITH HEAVY FIGHTER ESCORTS CROSSED THE COAST IN DAYLIGHT RAIDS...

ACHTUNG! SPITFIRES!

BIGGIN HILL AIRFIELD, KENT. ONE OF THE LEADING FIGHTER STATIONS.

WHAT A SHAMBLES!

LOOK, HERE COMES THE GRAND OLD MAN HIMSELF!

THEY'RE BASHING US ABOUT A BIT, SIR, BUT THEY CAN'T KEEP OUR PLANES OUT OF THE SKY!

THE FATE OF THE COUNTRY NOW RESTS WITH YOU — OUR FIGHTER PILOTS. GOD BE WITH ALL OF YOU!

TO BE CONTINUED.

The Blitz
and
The Battle of Crete

*St Paul's rose majestic amidst fire as the
Cathedral Watch fought to save the great church.*

EAGLE 18 *April* 1958

The HAPPY WARRIOR

The true life story of
SIR WINSTON CHURCHILL

August, 1940. The Battle of France is ended and the Battle of Britain is raging! Daily, great waves of German bombers with fighter escorts are launched against the defences and airfields of Southern England. Prime Minister Churchill visits the forward stations of Fighter Command as the great battle for air supremacy nears its climax . . . .

TOLD BY CLIFFORD MAKINS
DRAWN BY FRANK BELLAMY

ALL No. 11 GROUP AIRFIELDS ARE BEING BOMBED INCESSANTLY.

ENEMY LOSSES ARE HEAVY — BUT SO ARE OURS. CAN WE REPLACE OUR LOST PLANES?

TAKE HEART! LORD BEAVERBROOK IS WORKING MIRACLES WITH THE AIRCRAFT INDUSTRY. THE LUFTWAFFE WILL NEVER RULE THESE SKIES!

GERMAN AIR ATTACKS BECAME BIGGER AND FIERCER . . . . .

THERE THEY ARE, CHAPS — DEAD AHEAD! NO MORE THAN 500 OF 'EM! HERE WE GO!

MEANWHILE, BOMBER COMMAND, WITH LIMITED RESOURCES, STRUCK BACK.

OUR BRITISH AIRMEN ARE TURNING THE TIDE OF THE WORLD WAR BY THEIR PROWESS AND DEVOTION . . . *NEVER IN THE FIELD OF HUMAN CONFLICT HAS SO MUCH BEEN OWED BY SO MANY TO SO FEW!*

AND HITLER RAGED IN BERLIN . . .

WE HAVE FAILED TO SHOOT THE R.A.F FROM THE SKIES — ON THE CONTRARY, THEY HAVE MORE PLANES THAN EVER! THE INVASION MUST BE POSTPONED. NOW LET OUR BOMBERS RAZE LONDON TO THE GROUND. WE WILL GIVE THAT WARMONGER CHURCHILL A LESSON! *BOMB LONDON!*

THE BLITZ!

EARLY IN SEPTEMBER, THE LUFTWAFFE SWITCHED THEIR ATTACKS TO LONDON. EVERY NIGHT THROUGHOUT THE AUTUMN AND THE WINTER BOMBS RAINED DOWN ON THE GREATEST CAPITAL CITY IN THE WORLD . . .

THE PRIME MINISTER WAS STILL AT No. 10 DOWNING STREET . . .

GET YOUR TIN HATS! WE'RE GOING ON THE ROOF!

PALL MALL IS BLAZING FROM END TO END!

GREAT SCOTT! WHAT A SIGHT!

WINSTON! COME ON DOWN. THIS IS NO TIME FOR YOU TO RISK YOUR NECK!

WE MUST FACE THE FACT THAT LONDON MAY BE UTTERLY DESTROYED. EVERYTHING THAT IS HUMANLY POSSIBLE MUST BE DONE TO PROTECT AND COMFORT THE BRAVE PEOPLE OF THIS GREAT CITY!

TO BE CONTINUED

EAGLE 25 April 1958

The HAPPY WARRIOR

The true life story of
SIR WINSTON CHURCHILL

WINTER, 1940.

The massive daylight raids launched by German bombers and fighters throughout the summer have been defeated by the R.A.F.'s Spitfires and Hurricanes. Now the might of the Luftwaffe is turned on London and the great cities of Britain. Prime Minister Churchill, determined to stay at his post in Whitehall, sees large areas of London bombed and burned.

TOLD BY CLIFFORD MAKINS
DRAWN BY FRANK BELLAMY

NOT ONLY LONDON IS THREATENED WITH DESTRUCTION. THE WHOLE COUNTRY FACES A TERRIBLE ORDEAL. OUR GREAT CITIES WILL BE BOMBED INCESSANTLY. ANOTHER GRIM PHASE IS BEGINNING.

Night bombing raids were widespread. Coventry, Birmingham, Bristol, Southampton and Liverpool – these and many other towns and cities suffered heavily. Then, in December, came the fiercest of them all – the great fire raid on the City of London.

THE ANCIENT GUILDHALL WAS A SEA OF FLAMES...

FLEET STREET...

LOOK AT ST BRIDE'S – BLAZING LIKE A BONFIRE!

ST PAUL'S WILL BE THE NEXT TO GO!

ST PAUL'S ROSE MAJESTIC AMIDST FIRE AS THE CATHEDRAL WATCH FOUGHT TO SAVE THE GREAT CHURCH.

AND AT DAWN...

THANK GOD, THE OLD CHURCH IS STILL STANDING!

A MIRACLE.

GOOD OLD WINNIE!

WE CAN TAKE IT!

AND GIVE IT 'EM BACK!

WE WILL GIVE IT 'EM BACK ALL RIGHT! WE WILL REPAY THE DEBT TENFOLD, NAY, TWENTY FOLD. ALAS FOR POOR HUMANITY!

Meanwhile, the war spread across the world. In the Western Desert British troops, under Wavell, shattered the Italian Army, and the Italian Navy was badly mauled by the British Fleet. But Hitler was also active...

THE INVASION OF BRITAIN IS POSTPONED INDEFINITELY. WE MUST EXTEND THE WAR TO THE EAST!

FIRST THE BALKANS. WE MUST OCCUPY YUGOSLAVIA, BY FORCE IF NECESSARY, AND THEN CONQUER GREECE.

THEN WE SMASH THE BRITISH ARMY IN NORTH AFRICA. THIS MEANS WE HOLD SUEZ AND CONTROL THE MIDDLE EAST.

BUT, FUEHRER, IN THE WESTERN DESERT OUR ITALIAN ALLIES HAVE BEEN ROUTED!

PRECISELY! WE WILL GIVE THEM A STIFFENING OF GERMAN ARMOUR. I HAVE A FINE MAN FOR THE JOB – GENERAL ROMMEL!

LATER, IN LONDON...

WELL, WINSTON, WE'RE WEATHERING THE STORM ON THE HOME FRONT VERY WELL!

YES, BUT WE MUST NOW LOOK BEYOND THESE SHORES. GENERAL ROMMEL HAS ARRIVED IN AFRICA AND NAZI FORCES ARE CONCENTRATING IN THE BALKANS. THERE WILL BE BITTER FIGHTING SOON!

TO BE CONTINUED.

EAGLE 9 May 1958

The HAPPY WARRIOR

The true life story of
SIR WINSTON CHURCHILL

May, 1941. Britain is at bay in the Mediterranean area. Rommel's panzers have surged across the Libyan desert to the Egyptian frontier, and German armies have conquered Greece and Yugoslavia. Prime Minister Churchill urges the strongest resistance in the vital island of Crete, manned by 30,000 Imperial troops under the command of General Freyberg. In their bid to capture the island, the Germans launch the biggest-ever air assault . . .

TOLD BY CLIFFORD MAKINS. DRAWN BY FRANK BELLAMY.

HERE COME THE JERRIES AGAIN!

STAND FAST, LADS! WE'VE GOT TO STOP 'EM!

GET DOWN, CHAPS! FIGHTERS!

GENERAL FREYBERG'S H.Q., CRETE.

THEY'RE BOMBING US TO BLAZES, BUT WE'RE STILL HANGING ON, THANK GOD!

THE BRITISH FLEET WAS HEAVILY AND INCESSANTLY BOMBED OFF CRETE. H.M.S. WARSPITE WAS BADLY DAMAGED.

LONDON. CHURCHILL WATCHED THE COURSE OF EVENTS WITH GREAT FEELING.

IT LOOKS BLACK IN CRETE. THE ENEMY HAS ABSOLUTE CONTROL OF THE AIR.

IT'S A MOST VITAL BATTLE! THERE'S A GRAVE DANGER THAT THE MEDITERRANEAN FLEET MAY BE BADLY CRIPPLED BUT, IF WE STICK IT OUT, WE MAY YET WIN THE DAY!

TELEGRAPH FREYBERG: 'YOUR GLORIOUS DEFENCE COMMANDS ADMIRATION IN EVERY LAND. WE KNOW ENEMY IS HARD PRESSED. ALL AID IN OUR POWER IS BEING SENT.'

TO COMMANDERS-IN-CHIEF MIDDLE EAST: 'VICTORY IN CRETE ESSENTIAL AT THIS TURNING POINT IN THE WAR. KEEP HURLING IN ALL AID YOU CAN.'

ALAS, IT'S HOPELESS. OUR FRONT AT CANEA HAS COLLAPSED, OUR FORCES AT HERAKLION ARE SURROUNDED. WE MUST GET OUT — IF THERE'S TIME!

BUT, THAT VERY DAY, THE GALLANT FREYBERG WAS FORCED TO ADMIT DEFEAT.

IN LONDON . . .

IT IS THE END IN CRETE. WE HAVE LOST THE BATTLE. ANOTHER DEFEAT! ANOTHER WITHDRAWAL!

17,000 Imperial troops were evacuated from Crete, leaving behind 13,000 comrades, killed, wounded and captured. The Navy lost three cruisers and six destroyers. Meanwhile, the German battleship Bismark was sunk in the Atlantic. But Churchill faced a storm in the House . . .

IN VIEW OF THE OUTCOME, WHY WAS CRETE DEFENDED AT ALL? WAS IT NOT A LOST CAUSE? HAVE WE NOT SACRIFICED OUR MEN AND IMPERILLED OUR FLEET FOR NOTHING?

WHAT WOULD HAVE BEEN SAID IF WE HAD GIVEN UP THE ISLAND OF CRETE WITHOUT FIRING A SHOT? WE SHOULD HAVE BEEN TOLD THAT THIS PUSILLANIMOUS FLIGHT HAD SURRENDERED TO THE ENEMY THE KEY OF THE EASTERN MEDITERRANEAN!

TO BE CONTINUED.

EAGLE 16 *May 1958*

The HAPPY WARRIOR

The true life story of
SIR WINSTON CHURCHILL

May, 1941. The great Battle of Crete has been fought and lost, but the Commonwealth troops have struck a mortal blow at German airborne power. The Fleet, though suffering serious losses, still controls the Mediterranean. But the defeat has caused concern in the House, and Prime Minister Churchill is forced to make an extensive review of the latest situation...

TOLD BY CLIFFORD MAKINS
DRAWN BY FRANK BELLAMY

I AM SURE IT WILL BE FOUND THAT THIS SOMBRE AND FEROCIOUS BATTLE OF CRETE... WAS WELL WORTH FIGHTING AND THAT IT WILL HAVE AN EXTREMELY IMPORTANT EFFECT ON THE WHOLE DEFENCE OF THE NILE VALLEY.

Churchill's masterly survey of the Battle of Crete completely reassured the House. Meanwhile, in Berlin, Hitler was planning another colossal war...

BRITAIN MAY NOT BE BEATEN YET, BUT WE ARE THE MASTERS OF EUROPE—NOTHING CAN CHANGE THAT. NOW IS THE TIME TO STRIKE EAST — AT RUSSIA!

FUEHRER, IT IS A FEARFUL UNDERTAKING TO ATTACK RUSSIA.

WHY, WE HAVE ONLY TO KICK IN THE DOOR AND THE WHOLE ROTTEN STRUCTURE WILL COME TUMBLING DOWN. ONE SINGLE CAMPAIGN WILL SUFFICE!

JUNE 22nd, 1941

OPERATION BARBAROSSA!

GERMAN ATTACK ON RUSSIA. 164 DIVISIONS SUPPORTED BY 2,700 AIRCRAFT!

AS IN THE POLISH CAMPAIGN, THE LUFTWAFFE STRUCK SAVAGE BLOWS AT ALL AIRFIELDS.

ENGLAND. GENERAL DILL HURRIED DOWN TO CHEQUERS WITH DETAILED NEWS.

THE GERMANS HAVE ATTACKED ON A VAST FRONT AND ARE ADVANCING AT GREAT SPEED!

I EXPECTED IT! I MUST BROADCAST TO THE NATION TONIGHT.

WE ARE RESOLVED TO DESTROY HITLER AND EVERY VESTIGE OF THE NAZI REGIME...... IT FOLLOWS, THEREFORE, THAT WE SHALL GIVE WHATEVER HELP WE CAN TO RUSSIA.. ...LET US REDOUBLE OUR EXERTIONS AND STRIKE WITH UNITED STRENGTH!

Within a month, the Germans were 300 miles into Russia. Great stores of British arms and supplies were sent to Russia. In the Western Desert, Auchinleck had replaced Wavell. Then, at a Cabinet meeting...

PRESIDENT ROOSEVELT HAS SUGGESTED THAT I MEET HIM IN NEWFOUNDLAND. I MOST EARNESTLY DESIRE THE CABINET'S APPROVAL OF THIS VENTURE, WHICH MUST SURELY BIND BRITAIN AND THE UNITED STATES CLOSER THAN EVER BEFORE.

EARLY IN AUGUST, THE PRIME MINISTER LEFT BRITAIN IN THE MIGHTY BATTLESHIP *PRINCE OF WALES*.

TO BE CONTINUED.

D-Day

At Tehran, Churchill, Roosevelt and Stalin have reached agreement on plans to launch a concerted attack on Germany to end the war. Returning from the conference, the Prime Minister falls dangerously ill...

EAGLE 23 May 1958

The HAPPY WARRIOR

The true life story of
SIR WINSTON CHURCHILL

August, 1941. The power of the German war-machine is now at full blast. Following their conquest of Crete, the Nazis launch a gigantic offensive against Russia and, in a short time, advance hundreds of miles. Meanwhile, Prime Minister Churchill leaves Scapa Flow in the mighty battleship *Prince of Wales* to meet the President of the United States, Mr Roosevelt, at a secret rendezvous off Newfoundland . . .

TOLD BY CLIFFORD MAKINS
DRAWN BY FRANK BELLAMY

MAGNIFICENT! THIS IS A REAL HOLIDAY FOR ME!

I'M GLAD YOU'RE ENJOYING YOURSELF, MR CHURCHILL! I ONLY HOPE WE STEER CLEAR OF TROUBLE!

A FEW DAYS LATER . . .

WE'RE HERE —PLACENTIA BAY, NEWFOUNDLAND!

MR PRESIDENT!

PRIME MINISTER —IT'S GOOD TO SEE YOU!

. . STABLISH OUR HEARTS, O GOD, IN THE DAY OF BATTLE, AND STRENGTHEN OUR RESOLVE, THAT WE FIGHT NOT IN ENMITY AGAINST MEN BUT AGAINST THE POWERS OF DARKNESS ENSLAVING THE SOULS OF MEN!

SUNDAY, AUGUST 10th. DIVINE SERVICE FOR OFFICERS AND MEN OF THE BRITISH AND AMERICAN NAVIES ON BOARD THE *PRINCE OF WALES*.

Between them, the President and the Prime Minister devised the historic 'Atlantic Charter' which, in the name of Great Britain and the United States of America, gave suffering humanity hopes of a better world. Then Churchill sailed home to reflect on a terrible new menace which was brewing . . .

WE ARE FACING A NEW SERIOUS THREAT, IN THE FAR EAST. THERE IS EVERY INDICATION THAT JAPAN IS ABOUT TO ENTER THE WAR ON THE SIDE OF GERMANY AND ITALY. WE ARE GRIEVOUSLY UNDERMANNED IN THIS THEATRE AND SHALL DO WELL TO HOLD OUR OWN.

JAPANESE AIR ATTACKS ON PEARL HARBOUR HAWAII AND ON BRITISH POSSESSIONS IN MALAYA!

AT CHEQUERS, THE PRIME MINISTER'S COUNTRY RESIDENCE . . .

SIR, THE PRESIDENT OF THE UNITED STATES IS CALLING FROM WASHINGTON!

WE ARE WITH YOU TO THE END! GOD BE WITH YOU TOO! GOODBYE!

YES, IT'S TRUE ALL RIGHT. THE JAPANESE HAVE ATTACKED US AT PEARL HARBOUR AND CRIPPLED OUR FLEET! WE ARE ALL IN THE SAME BOAT NOW.

MEANWHILE, THE *PRINCE OF WALES* AND THE BATTLECRUISER *REPULSE* WERE SEEKING JAPANESE TRANSPORTS OFF MALAYA.

ENEMY AIRCRAFT APPROACHING!

WITHOUT AIR SUPPORT, THE TWO CAPITAL SHIPS FOUGHT A DESPERATE, LOSING BATTLE . . .

SOME HOURS LATER, AT THE ADMIRALTY . . .

SIR, TERRIBLE NEWS. WE HAVE LOST THE *PRINCE OF WALES* AND THE *REPULSE*.

GOOD GOD, WHAT A BITTER BLOW! I MUST 'PHONE THE PRIME MINISTER IMMEDIATELY.

TO BE CONTINUED.

EAGLE 30 *May 1958*

The HAPPY WARRIOR

The true life story of
SIR WINSTON CHURCHILL

December, 1941. German armies are deep into Russia, and Rommel is still undefeated in the Western Desert. Prime Minister Churchill crosses the Atlantic for the first of his famous conferences with President Roosevelt. Then Japan enters the war, striking in the Far East at both Britain and America. Grave news reaches the Admiralty concerning the *Prince of Wales* and the *Repulse*, which have been sent out to Malaya . . .

TOLD BY CLIFFORD MAKINS
DRAWN BY FRANK BELLAMY

PRIME MINISTER, THE *PRINCE OF WALES* AND THE *REPULSE* HAVE BEEN SUNK BY THE JAPANESE!

WHAT A TRAGIC LOSS!

THE AMERICAN FLEET CRIPPLED AT PEARL HARBOUR! TWO OF OUR FINEST SHIPS SUNK OFF MALAYA! NOW THE JAPANESE CONTROL THE PACIFIC OCEAN. I MUST SEE PRESIDENT ROOSEVELT AGAIN IMMEDIATELY!

Churchill went to Washington with his Chiefs of Staff in the battleship *Duke of York*. Now all the leading nations were at war: Britain, America and Russia versus Germany, Italy and Japan. After searching talks, Churchill returned by air . . .

BERMUDA . . .

YOU KNOW WHAT HE'S LIKE — ONCE HIS MIND'S MADE UP, THERE'S NO STOPPING HIM!

IT'S A FANTASTIC RISK FOR THE P.M. TO FLY HOME — WHY IT'S 3,500 MILES!

NOW THAT AMERICA IS ON OUR SIDE, I HAVE NO DOUBT THAT WE SHALL WIN THE WAR — BUT, MEANWHILE, WE MUST SUFFER A TERRIBLE ONSLAUGHT FROM JAPAN.

WINSTON, YOU HAVE THE LOYALTY AND CONFIDENCE OF US ALL.

BACK IN LONDON . . .

THE JAPANESE ARE SWARMING LIKE ANTS THROUGH MALAYA. SINGAPORE IS IN GRAVE PERIL.

WE MUST FIGHT THERE TO THE BITTER END — AT ALL COSTS.

SINGAPORE ISLAND. JAPANESE TROOPS IN LANDING-CRAFT SURGED ACROSS THE STRAITS FROM THE MAINLAND.

WELL DONE, SERGEANT — KEEP 'EM AT BAY AS LONG AS YOU CAN!

THE MEN ARE ALL IN — THEY HAVEN'T SLEPT FOR THREE DAYS.

SINGAPORE TOWN — H.Q. GENERAL PERCIVAL, G.O.C. MALAYA.

THE TROOPS ARE FALLING BACK EVERYWHERE, SIR, AND STORES AND AMMUNITION ARE NEARLY EXHAUSTED.

I FEAR THE END IS AT HAND.

THE NEXT DAY, FEB. 15th., 1942.

TO GENERAL WAVELL, SUPREME COMMANDER, SOUTH-EAST ASIA: 'WATER, PETROL, FOOD AND AMMUNITION PRACTICALLY FINISHED. UNABLE THEREFORE TO CONTINUE THE FIGHTING ANY LONGER. ALL RANKS HAVE DONE THEIR BEST AND ARE GRATEFUL FOR YOUR HELP'.

AND SO THE GREAT FORTRESS OF SINGAPORE CAPITULATED. THOUSANDS OF BRITISH AND COMMONWEALTH TROOPS PASSED INTO CAPTIVITY.

After the defeat in Malaya, the British lost Burma. The Dutch East Indies fell and, with the invasion of New Guinea, Australia was in peril.

I BELIEVE WITH ALL MY HEART THAT WE SHALL WIN THE WAR. UP TO NOW WE HAVE LOST ALL THE BATTLES, BUT SOON THE TIDE WILL TURN. OUT OF THE BITTERNESS OF DEFEAT, THE FINAL VICTORY WILL COME. I KNOW IT!

TO BE CONTINUED.

EAGLE 6 June 1958

The HAPPY WARRIOR

The true life story of
SIR WINSTON CHURCHILL

MAY, 1942

Britain and America are on the defensive before the onslaught of Japan and the other Axis powers. Following the crippling of the U.S. fleet at Pearl Harbour, the great fortress of Singapore falls to the Japanese. Then Burma and the Dutch East Indies are occupied, and India and Australia are threatened. The whole British Empire is in grave peril, but Prime Minister Churchill is still undaunted and believes in ultimate victory . . .

TOLD BY CLIFFORD MAKINS
DRAWN BY FRANK BELLAMY

WHILE I HAVE THE CONFIDENCE OF THE BRITISH PEOPLE, I SHALL NEVER CONCEAL FROM THEM THE TRUTH ABOUT THE BLOWS WE ARE SUFFERING AND MUST GO ON SUFFERING.

MEETING OF THE WAR CABINET, LONDON.

WE MUST ATTACK AND DESTROY ROMMEL'S ARMY IN THE WESTERN DESERT. IT IS VITAL THAT GENERAL AUCHINLECK ATTACKS WITHOUT DELAY!

AUCHINLECK FEELS THAT OUR ARMY WILL HAVE THE BEST CHANCE IF ROMMEL ATTACKS FIRST.

I DON'T SHARE THAT VIEW AT ALL! WHILE ROMMEL IS GETTING READY, WE SHOULD HIT HIM —HARD!

WESTERN DESERT, A FEW WEEKS LATER — ROMMEL DID STRIKE FIRST!

WE HAVE WON THE DAY! THE BRITISH ARMOUR HAS BEEN ANNIHILATED. NOW WE WILL TAKE TOBRUK.

THE NEXT DAY, GERMAN TANKS PENETRATED THE DEFENCES OF TOBRUK...

MEANWHILE, CHURCHILL WAS IN WASHINGTON WITH PRESIDENT ROOSEVELT WHEN A TELEGRAM ARRIVED...

GEE—BAD NEWS FOR THE BRITISH! THIS SHOULD GO TO THE PRESIDENT'S ROOM IMMEDIATELY.

TOBRUK HAS SURRENDERED WITH 25,000 MEN TAKEN PRISONER.

WHAT CAN WE DO TO HELP?

MR PRESIDENT, GIVE US AS MANY SHERMAN TANKS AS YOU CAN SPARE AND SHIP THEM TO THE MIDDLE EAST, AS SOON AS POSSIBLE.

Churchill flew back to England, where he met uneasiness in the country and a storm in the House of Commons. But, following a great speech from the Prime Minister, a motion of no confidence was resoundingly defeated.

THIS IS THE MOMENT WHEN WE RISE OR FALL. I WILL FLY TO EGYPT MYSELF TO SIZE UP THE SITUATION — AND AFTER THAT I SHALL GO TO SEE STALIN IN MOSCOW.

CAIRO – A FEW DAYS LATER.

HERE COMES CHURCHILL'S 'PLANE. HE'S DONE IT AGAIN!

NOW WE SHALL SEE SOME FIREWORKS!

TO BE CONTINUED.

EAGLE 13 June 1958

The HAPPY WARRIOR

The true life story of
SIR WINSTON CHURCHILL

For the time being, Japanese aggression in the Far East has been checked, and the Americans have won a great naval victory off Midway Island. But in the Western Desert, Rommel and his Africa Corps have won their biggest victory to date – the fortress of Tobruk has fallen and Egypt is menaced. Churchill flies to Egypt in order to make far-reaching decisions.

TOLD BY CLIFFORD MAKINS
DRAWN BY FRANK BELLAMY

WINSTON, WHEN WE GET TO THE EMBASSY, I ADVISE A SHORT REST.

CERTAINLY NOT— I'VE NEVER FELT BETTER! WE WILL GET STRAIGHT DOWN TO BUSINESS.

BRITISH EMBASSY, CAIRO. TWO DAYS LATER.

ROMMEL, ROMMEL, ROMMEL! WHAT ELSE MATTERS BUT BEATING HIM? WE MUST MAKE SWEEPING CHANGES IN OUR HIGH COMMAND.

After high-level discussions, in which General Smuts played a prominent part, General Auchinleck was relieved of his command. General Alexander replaced him, and General Montgomery was given command of the Eighth Army. Then Churchill set off for Moscow . . .

MOSCOW! I DOUBT IF WE SHALL GET A WARM RECEPTION HERE.

LATER, IN THE KREMLIN, FIERY DISCUSSIONS WITH STALIN TOOK PLACE.

THE BRITISH ARE AFRAID OF FIGHTING GERMANS! THEY SHOULD TRY IT SOME TIME, LIKE THE RUSSIANS – IT IS NOT TOO BAD!

BECAUSE OF THE BRAVERY OF THE RUSSIAN ARMY, I PARDON MR STALIN'S FOOLISH REMARKS –BUT HE IS TALKING NONSENSE.

AGREEMENT WAS REACHED IN THE END.

GOODBYE! TELL MR STALIN THAT I HAVE UNSHAKABLE FAITH IN THE TRIUMPH OF RUSSIA, BRITAIN AND AMERICA AGAINST OUR COMMON ENEMIES.

Churchill flew back to Cairo to meet Alexander and Montgomery. There the great strategy for the defeat of Rommel was finally perfected. American intervention in Africa was to come a little later on. After visiting troops, the Premier flew home.

OCTOBER 23rd, 1942. GENERAL MONTGOMERY'S TACTICAL H.Q. IN THE WESTERN DESERT.

THE BATTLE WHICH IS NOW ABOUT TO BEGIN WILL BE ONE OF THE DECISIVE BATTLES OF HISTORY. IT WILL BE THE TURNING POINT OF THE WAR...THE LORD MIGHTY IN BATTLE WILL GIVE US THE VICTORY.

THE BATTLE OF ALAMEIN

ON A 7,000-YARD FRONT, NEARLY 1,000 GUNS OPENED FIRE.

AS THE BATTLE RAGED, HUGE BOMBING ATTACKS POUNDED ENEMY POSITIONS.

ROMMEL IS CRACKING! ONE GOOD, HARD BLOW AND HIS ARMY WILL BE FINISHED FOR EVER.

NOVEMBER 3rd. MONTGOMERY'S ARMOUR CRASHED THROUGH THE GERMAN LINES...

THEY'RE ON THE RUN, MATE — THEY'RE ON THE RUN!

TO BE CONTINUED.

EAGLE 20 June 1958

The HAPPY WARRIOR

The true life story of
SIR WINSTON CHURCHILL

OCTOBER — NOVEMBER, 1942
BATTLE OF ALAMEIN!

Following Churchill's visit to Cairo, sweeping changes are made in the Middle East Command. General Alexander replaces General Auchinleck as supreme commander, and General Montgomery is placed in command of the Eighth Army. Montgomery starts the Battle of Alamein with a stupendous artillery barrage. After several days of very bitter fighting, Rommel is put to flight . . . .

TOLD BY CLIFFORD MAKINS
DRAWN BY FRANK BELLAMY

WE HAVE SMASHED THE GERMAN AND ITALIAN ARMY, AND SOON THE REMNANTS WILL BE PUSHED OUT OF EGYPT!

THE VICTORIOUS EIGHTH ARMY CHASED ROMMEL OUT OF EGYPT

GENERAL ALEXANDER, WITH HIS BRILLIANT COMRADE AND LIEUTENANT, GENERAL MONTGOMERY, HAS GAINED A GLORIOUS AND DECISIVE VICTORY.

GENERAL ROMMEL'S H.Q.

GENERAL ROMMEL, WE HAVE EIGHTY TANKS LEFT AGAINST SIX HUNDRED BRITISH!

IT IS THE END OF THE AFRICA CORPS! WE MUST KEEP ON RUNNING.

IF ONLY HITLER HAD GIVEN ME A FRACTION OF THE TROOPS HE HAS THROWN AGAINST RUSSIA, THE VICTORY WOULD HAVE BEEN OURS. STILL, WE MUST FIGHT WHILE WE CAN!

SPAIN

Casablanca
Mogador
Agadir
MOROCCO
Oran
Algiers
Philipperille
ALGERIA
TUNISIA

FIERCE RESISTANCE WAS MET AT ALGIERS, WHEN H.M.S. BROKE AND MALCOM TRIED TO LAND AMERICAN TROOPS IN THE HARBOUR.

AT ORAN, AN AMERICAN TASK FORCE WAS LANDED IN FACE OF STERN OPPOSITION. H.M.S. RODNEY PLAYED A LEADING PART IN THE BOMBARDMENT.

Meanwhile, on November 7th, a new front was opened in Africa. Powerful British and American forces commanded by General Eisenhower landed at many points in French North Africa.

NOVEMBER 29th. CHURCHILL BROADCASTS TO THE WORLD.

WITH HITLER IN MUNICH...

TOO LATE! THE FRENCH HAVE DESTROYED THEIR FLEET.

HERR FUEHRER, THE BRITISH AND AMERICANS ARE NOW FIRMLY ESTABLISHED IN AFRICA — MONTGOMERY IN THE EAST AND EISENHOWER IN THE WEST.

WE WILL NOT YIELD! WE MUST POUR MORE TROOPS INTO AFRICA, AND WE MUST SEIZE THE FRENCH FLEET AT TOULON.

EARLY ON NOVEMBER 27th, GERMAN FORCES DASHED THROUGH UNOCCUPIED FRANCE, ONLY TO FIND THAT THE FRENCH FLEET HAD ALREADY BEEN SCUTTLED AT TOULON.

In the meantime, after the heroic defence of Stalingrad, Russian troops began to take the offensive along a vast front. All the world over, the initiative was slowly but surely passing to the allies.

THE BRITISH PEOPLE HAVE PROVED THEY CAN STAND DEFEAT ...I SEE NO REASON AT ALL WHY WE SHOULD NOT SHOW OURSELVES EQUALLY RESOLUTE AND ACTIVE IN THE FACE OF VICTORY!

TO BE CONTINUED.

EAGLE 27 June 1958

The HAPPY WARRIOR

The true life story of
SIR WINSTON CHURCHILL

With the dawn of 1943, the tide of war has turned in favour of the Allies. The Russians are on the offensive, the 8th Army has destroyed the Africa Corps and powerful Anglo-American forces have landed in French North Africa. Prime Minister Churchill is jubilant, as he ponders the next stage of the titanic struggle to liberate mankind . . . .

TOLD BY CLIFFORD MAKINS
DRAWN BY FRANK BELLAMY

THE END IS IN SIGHT IN AFRICA. OUR NEXT MOVE IS MOST VITAL! I MUST GO TO WASHINGTON AGAIN, TO TALK THINGS OVER WITH THE PRESIDENT.

WELL, THIS TIME YOU'RE NOT FLYING! THOSE ARE DOCTOR'S ORDERS, AND YOU MUST STICK TO THEM.

ALL RIGHT — THE QUEEN MARY IS SAILING TO NEW YORK WITH A LOAD OF GERMAN PRISONERS— I'LL KEEP THEM COMPANY!

THE GIANT LINER, WITH CHURCHILL AND HIS STAFF ABOARD, RACED ACROSS THE ATLANTIC...

MEANWHILE, OFF TUNISIA, BRITISH AND AMERICAN FIGHTERS WROUGHT HAVOC WITH GERMAN AIR TRANSPORT.

AT GENERAL ALEXANDER'S H.Q. IN NORTH AFRICA.

THE AXIS IS CRUMBLING EVERYWHERE! WE SHALL SOON HAVE GOOD NEWS FOR WINSTON.

A FEW DAYS LATER.

AFRICA IS REDEEMED! NOW WE WILL STRIKE AT EUROPE WITH ALL OUR MIGHT.

JULY — AUGUST
INVASION AND CONQUEST OF SICILY

Sicily

TO THE PRIME MINISTER, WASHINGTON— 'SIR, IT IS MY DUTY TO REPORT THAT THE TUNISIAN CAMPAIGN IS OVER. ALL ENEMY RESISTANCE HAS CEASED. WE ARE MASTERS OF THE NORTH AFRICAN SHORES.'

AND AT HITLER'S HEADQUARTERS IN EAST PRUSSIA...

HERR FUEHRER! MUSSOLINI IS DEPOSED AND MARSHAL BADOGLIO HAS FORMED A NEW ITALIAN GOVERNMENT.

TRAITORS! THEY WILL MAKE PEACE WITH BRITAIN AND AMERICA!

WE MUST BOLT THE BACK DOOR QUICKLY, POUR TROOPS INTO ITALY AND OCCUPY ROME!

SEPTEMBER! INVASION OF ITALY! AN ALLIED ARMADA SAILED INTO THE GULF OF SALERNO.

Italy soon surrendered, but a powerful German army gripped the country and offered stern resistance in the South to the invading Allies. Meanwhile, Churchill returned to England in the battle-cruiser *Renown* . . .

WE HAVE BITTEN 300 MILES OFF ITALY'S BOOT! ITALY IS OUT OF THE WAR, BUT GERMANY WILL FIGHT TO THE END — AND IT WILL BE A BITTER END!

TO BE CONTINUED.

45

Victory

...at the height of the victory celebrations,
Winston Churchill is cast from power...

EAGLE 9 August 1958

The HAPPY WARRIOR

The true life story of **SIR WINSTON CHURCHILL**

OCTOBER, 1944.

The victorious Allied Armies have reclaimed France, and most of Holland and Belgium, from the Germans. But now, after this great victory, the offensive has come to a halt. Prime Minister Churchill emphasizes that much hard fighting lies ahead. Meanwhile, Hitler is planning a last, desperate assault in an effort to save the day for Germany.

TOLD BY CLIFFORD MAKINS
DRAWN BY FRANK BELLAMY

WE WILL LAUNCH A COUNTER-ATTACK IN THE ARDENNES EARLY IN DECEMBER. OUR OBJECTIVE IS THE RECAPTURE OF ANTWERP.

A BOLD PLAN INDEED, MEIN FUEHRER!

BUT WE HAVEN'T THE MEN, THE MACHINES — WE HAVEN'T THE PETROL!

I WILL NOT LISTEN TO DEFEATIST TALK! THE ATTACK WILL TAKE PLACE AS PLANNED. THE AMERICAN ARMIES WILL BE CUT IN TWO AND THE BRITISH ARMY ISOLATED. WAIT AND SEE!

O.K., FELLAS — THEY'RE COMING RIGHT AT US. NOW GIVE 'EM A ROUSING WELCOME!

THE GERMANS GATHERED STRENGTH AND, IN DECEMBER, STRUCK HARD IN THE ARDENNES...

BUT THE GERMAN COLUMNS SURGED ON.

AND IN LONDON...

THE GERMANS HAVE BROKEN THROUGH, ALL RIGHT — FIERCE FIGHTING AND CONFUSION EVERYWHERE.

I DO NOT THINK THEY WILL GET FAR. I WILL SPEAK TO EISENHOWER TONIGHT.

IT'S TOUGH GOING, BUT WE WILL HOLD THEM. I HAVE BRADLEY IN CHARGE IN THE SOUTH AND MONTGOMERY IN THE NORTH.

SPLENDID! BRITISH TROOPS WILL ALWAYS DEEM IT AN HONOUR TO ENTER THE SAME BATTLE AS THEIR AMERICAN FRIENDS.

The Ardennes battle was severe, but superb fighting qualities of American and British soldiers prevailed. By the end of January, 1945, the Germans were driven back with huge losses. Meanwhile, Russian armies were rolling through Poland in the East, and the Allies prepared their final assault on Hitler in the West.

CABINET MEETING, MARCH, 1945.

THE ALLIED ARMIES ARE ABOUT TO CROSS THE RHINE. I WANT TO BE WITH THE BRITISH ARMY AT THE CROSSING.

WINSTON, THESE TRIPS WILL BE THE DEATH OF YOU.

FIELD MARSHAL MONTGOMERY'S HEADQUARTERS, NEAR VENLO...

WE WILL FORCE THE RIVER AT TEN POINTS ON A TWENTY MILE FRONT. IN THE EARLY STAGES, TWO AIRBORNE DIVISIONS WILL BE DROPPED.

AH! I MUST SEE THAT!

NEXT DAY — *THE MIGHTY ATTACK WAS LAUNCHED. 2,000 PLANES TOOK PART IN THE ASSAULT, AND DROPPED 14,000 MEN WITH ARTILLERY AND ARMS...*

THERE THEY GO. AT LAST THE FULL FORCE OF WAR HAS COME TO GERMANY. THE END OF AN AWFUL TYRANNY IS AT HAND.

TO BE CONTINUED.

EAGLE 30 August 1958

The HAPPY WARRIOR

The true life story of **SIR WINSTON CHURCHILL**

JULY 26th, 1945

Germany has surrendered and the war in Europe is over. But, at the height of the victory celebrations, Winston Churchill is cast from power by the verdict of the people whose cause he has so nobly served. In the General Election, the Labour Party is returned with a huge majority, and the Tory Party leader is Prime Minister no more!

TOLD BY CLIFFORD MAKINS DRAWN BY FRANK BELLAMY

IT'S RATHER A BLOW, I MUST CONFESS, TO BE DISMISSED AT THE HOUR OF TRIUMPH. STILL, THERE IT IS! I SHALL SEEK AN AUDIENCE WITH THE KING TONIGHT.

HERE HE COMES!

LEADER OF THE OPPOSITION!

THE GREATEST ENGLISHMAN OF THEM ALL!

LATER THAT DAY, CHURCHILL LEFT BUCKINGHAM PALACE AFTER TENDERING HIS RESIGNATION TO THE KING...

AND A LITTLE LATER, AT NO. 10 DOWNING STREET...

IT ONLY REMAINS FOR ME TO EXPRESS TO THE BRITISH PEOPLE... MY PROFOUND GRATITUDE FOR THE UNFLINCHING, UNSWERVING SUPPORT WHICH THEY HAVE GIVEN ME DURING MY TASK, AND FOR THE MANY EXPRESSIONS OF KINDNESS WHICH THEY HAVE SHOWN TOWARDS THEIR SERVANT.

Meanwhile, the Allied forces were sweeping to victory in the Far East. Burma was reclaimed, and campaigns planned for the recapture of Malaya and the territories beyond. But the biggest onslaught of all was prepared against the heart of the Japanese Empire – still a powerful enemy.

WINSTON, DO YOU THINK THE JAPANESE WILL YIELD TO THE TERMS OF SURRENDER YOU DREW UP WITH TRUMAN AND CHIANG KAI-SHEK?

I DOUBT IT. I FEAR THEY ARE ABOUT TO SUFFER ONE OF THE MOST AWFUL BLOWS IN THE HISTORY OF MANKIND—BUT THE LIVES OF COUNTLESS ALLIED SOLDIERS WILL BE SPARED.

ON AUGUST 5th, AN ATOM BOMB WAS DROPPED ON HIROSHIMA, FOLLOWED ON AUGUST 9th BY A SECOND ATOM BOMB, ON NAGASAKI...

...AND THEN THE JAPANESE GOVERNMENT BROADCAST THEIR ACCEPTANCE OF THE ALLIED ULTIMATUM.

SEVERAL DAYS LATER, THE LEADER OF THE OPPOSITION MADE HIS FINAL REVIEW OF THE WAR...

THE MORROW OF SUCH A VICTORY AS WE HAVE GAINED IS A SPLENDID MOMENT BOTH IN OUR SMALL LIVES AND IN OUR GREAT HISTORY... WE HAVE COME SAFELY THROUGH THE WORST... "HOME IS THE SAILOR, HOME FROM SEA, AND THE HUNTER HOME FROM THE HILL."

WHAT A MAN! WHAT A LIFE! WHAT A GREAT CAREER HE'S HAD!

HAD? BELIEVE ME, OLD MAN, WE HAVEN'T SEEN THE LAST OF CHURCHILL YET — NOT BY A LONG CHALK!

1951 BACK IN POWER. PRIME MINISTER AGAIN!

1952 DEATH OF THE KING. CHURCHILL'S TRIBUTE!

HIS CONDUCT MAY WELL BE A MODEL AND A GUIDE TO CONSTITUTIONAL SOVEREIGNS THROUGHOUT THE WORLD TODAY, AND ALSO IN FUTURE GENERATIONS.

1953 KNIGHT OF THE GARTER.

1955 RESIGNATION! CHURCHILL MAKES WAY FOR EDEN.

GOD BLESS YOU, WINNIE! GOD BLESS YOU!

TO BE CONCLUDED

'*Whom neither shape of danger can dismay,*
Nor thought of tender happiness betray;
Who, not content that former worth stand fast,
Looks forward, persevering to the last...
And, while the mortal mist is gathering, draws
His breath in confidence of Heaven's applause:
This is THE HAPPY WARRIOR.'

WILLIAM WORDSWORTH

Why a 'Happy Warrior'?

Fittingly, it was Winston Churchill's friend Franklin Roosevelt who first uttered Wordsworth's poetical phrase "Happy Warrior" in a political context—or at least, he was the first to famously do so.

FDR anointed Governor Al Smith of New York with the sobriquet in 1924, in a speech nominating Smith as the Democratic candidate for president. (Smith lost the nomination but did gain a park in New York City named in his honor: Happy Warrior Playground.) Many years later, President Bill Clinton would refer to FDR himself as the Happy Warrior.

Today the appellation is political shorthand for one who exhibits gritty optimism and steadfastness. Perhaps no one fits the name so well as Winston Churchill—

> *Who, with a toward or untoward lot,*
> *Prosperous or adverse, to his wish or not—*
> *Plays, in the many games of life, that one*
> *Where what he most doth value must be won....*

Reverend Morris was wise to advise his young *Eagle* readers to seek out the poem, whose full title was "Character of The Happy Warrior." It was worth the read fifty years ago and is worth it now, 200 years after Wordsworth penned it.

Character of The Happy Warrior

WHO is the happy Warrior? Who is he

That every man in arms should wish to be?

—It is the generous Spirit, who, when brought

Among the tasks of real life, hath wrought

Upon the plan that pleased his boyish thought:

Whose high endeavours are an inward light

That makes the path before him always bright:

Who, with a natural instinct to discern

What knowledge can perform, is diligent to learn;

Abides by this resolve, and stops not there,

But makes his moral being his prime care;

Who, doomed to go in company with Pain,

And Fear, and Bloodshed, miserable train!

Turns his necessity to glorious gain;

In face of these doth exercise a power

Which is our human nature's highest dower;

Controls them and subdues, transmutes, bereaves

Of their bad influence, and their good receives:

By objects, which might force the soul to abate

Her feeling, rendered more compassionate;

Is placable—because occasions rise

So often that demand such sacrifice;

More skilful in self-knowledge, even more pure,

As tempted more; more able to endure,

As more exposed to suffering and distress;

Thence, also, more alive to tenderness.

—'Tis he whose law is reason; who depends

Upon that law as on the best of friends;

Whence, in a state where men are tempted still

To evil for a guard against worse ill,

And what in quality or act is best

Doth seldom on a right foundation rest,

He labours good on good to fix, and owes

To virtue every triumph that he knows:

—Who, if he rise to station of command,

Rises by open means; and there will stand

On honourable terms, or else retire,

And in himself possess his own desire;

Who comprehends his trust, and to the same

Keeps faithful with a singleness of aim;

And therefore does not stoop, nor lie in wait

For wealth, or honours, or for worldly state;

Why a 'Happy Warrior'?

Whom they must follow; on whose head must fall,

Like showers of manna, if they come at all:

Whose powers shed round him in the common strife,

Or mild concerns of ordinary life,

A constant influence, a peculiar grace;

But who, if he be called upon to face

Some awful moment to which Heaven has joined

Great issues, good or bad for human kind,

Is happy as a Lover; and attired

With sudden brightness, like a Man inspired;

And, through the heat of conflict, keeps the law

In calmness made, and sees what he foresaw;

Or if an unexpected call succeed,

Come when it will, is equal to the need:

—He who, though thus endued as with a sense

And faculty for storm and turbulence,

Is yet a Soul whose master-bias leans

To homefelt pleasures and to gentle scenes;

Sweet images! which, wheresoe'er he be,

Are at his heart; and such fidelity

It is his darling passion to approve;

More brave for this, that he hath much to love:—

'Tis, finally, the Man, who, lifted high,

Conspicuous object in a Nation's eye,

Or left unthought-of in obscurity,—

Who, with a toward or untoward lot,

Prosperous or adverse, to his wish or not—

Plays, in the many games of life, that one

Where what he most doth value must be won:

Whom neither shape of danger can dismay,

Nor thought of tender happiness betray;

Who, not content that former worth stand fast,

Looks forward, persevering to the last,

From well to better, daily self-surpast:

Who, whether praise of him must walk the earth

For ever, and to noble deeds give birth,

Or he must fall, to sleep without his fame,

And leave a dead unprofitable name—

Finds comfort in himself and in his cause;

And, while the mortal mist is gathering, draws

His breath in confidence of Heaven's applause:

This is the happy Warrior; this is He

That every Man in arms should wish to be.

– William Wordsworth, 1807

About Our Commentator

Richard M. Langworth is the founder of The Churchill Centre (winstonchurchill.org) and has served as the Chairman or Deputy Chairman of its Board of Trustees since 2000. He is also the longstanding editor of the Centre's quarterly journal, "Finest Hour."

Mr. Langworth published the first American edition of Churchill's *India* in 1990. He also compiled and annotated an exhaustive bibliography, *A Connoisseur's Guide to the Books of Sir Winston Churchill*, in 1998. The Levenger Press editions of Churchill's *The Dream* and *The Making of the Finest Hour* both feature introductions by Mr. Langworth. His most recent book, *Churchill by Himself: The Life, Times and Opinions of Winston Churchill in His Own Words*, chronicles Churchill's many famous quotations and includes historical context for each.

In 1998 Mr. Langworth was conferred the title of Commander of the Most Excellent Order of the British Empire (CBE) in honor of his work to preserve the Churchill legacy.

Uncommon Books
for Serious Readers

Levenger Press is the publishing arm of

LEVENGER

Levengerpress.com   800.544.0880